THE POWER OF FOREST BATHING

THE POWER OF FOREST BATHING

A COMPREHENSIVE GUIDE TO SHINRIN-YOKU, THE JAPANESE PRACTICE OF HEALING AND MINDFULNESS IN NATURE

HEALING POWER OF NATURE

NAOMI ROHAN

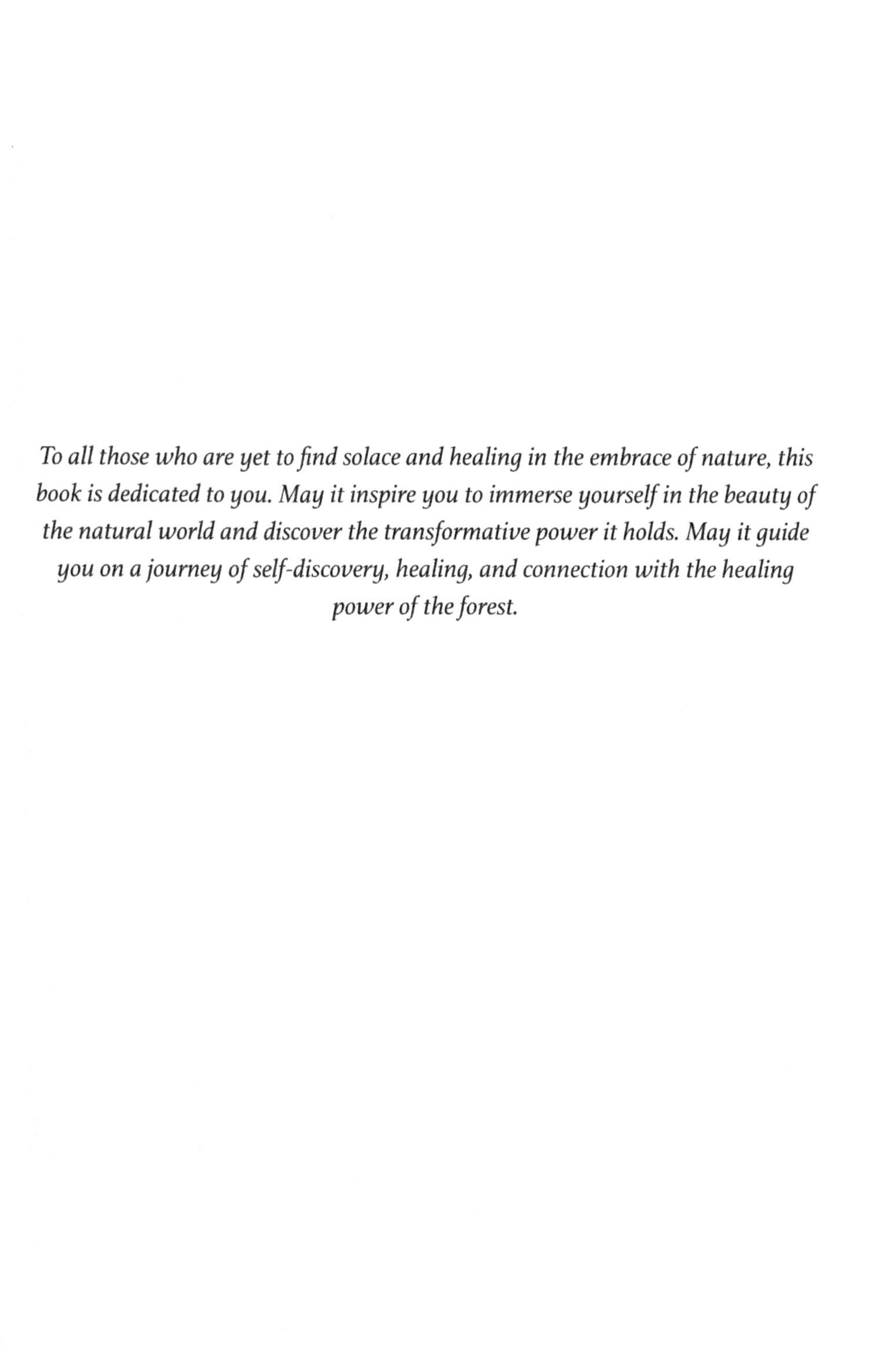

To all those who are yet to find solace and healing in the embrace of nature, this book is dedicated to you. May it inspire you to immerse yourself in the beauty of the natural world and discover the transformative power it holds. May it guide you on a journey of self-discovery, healing, and connection with the healing power of the forest.

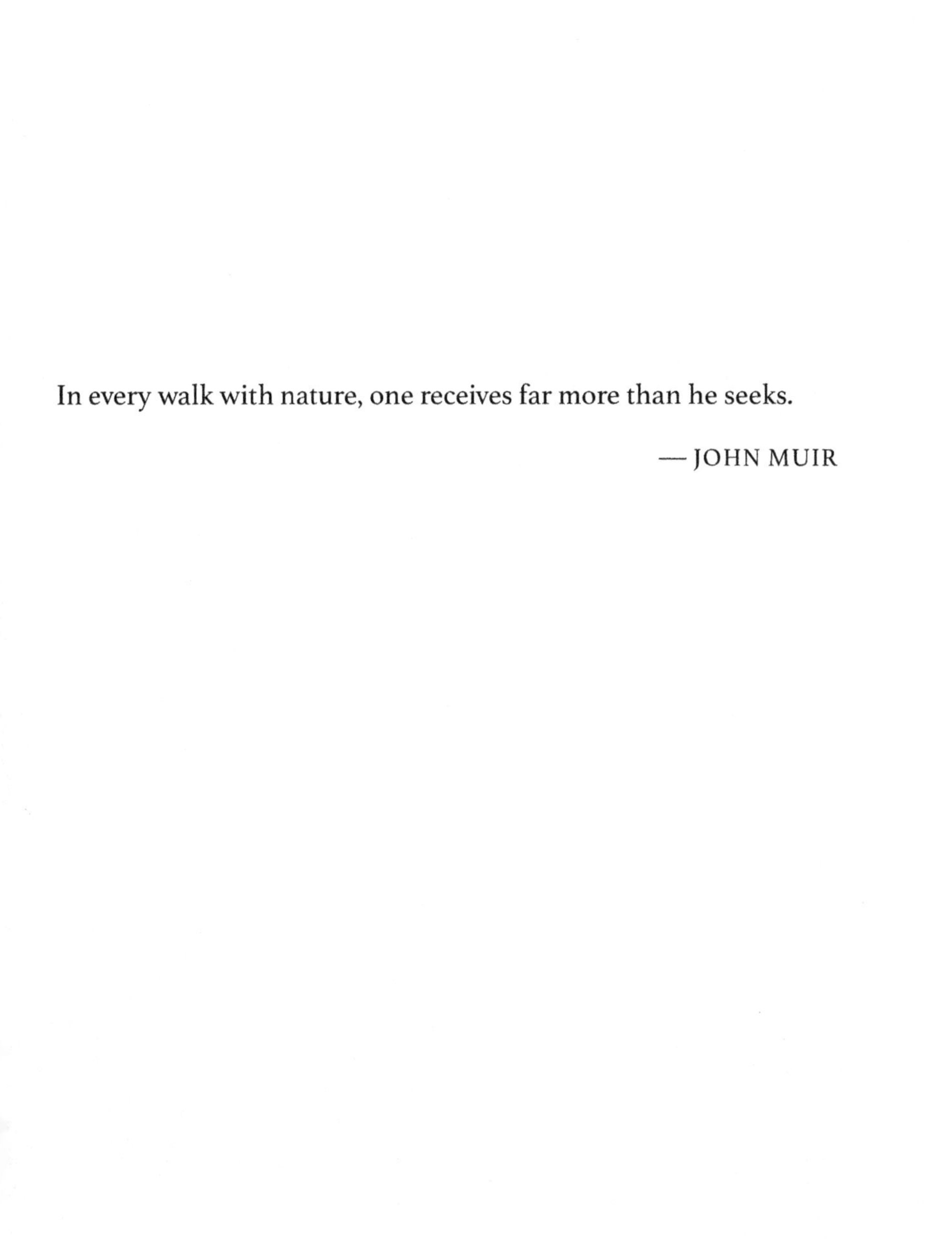

In every walk with nature, one receives far more than he seeks.

— JOHN MUIR

CONTENTS

FREE EBOOK BY NAOMI ROHAN: Nurtured by Nature

~~$9.99~~ FREE EBOOK

Scan the QR code below to download your free copy of Nurtured by Nature:

Or visit:
https://teilingenpress.wixsite.com/home/naomi-rohan

EMBRACING THE FOREST'S EMBRACE

In the calm stillness of the dawn, when the world is yet to stir from its slumber, the forest extends a whispered invitation. It is a call as ancient as the earth itself, a gentle beckoning that echoes through the rustling leaves and the murmuring brooks. It is an invitation to step away from the clamor of our bustling lives, leave behind the concrete jungles we inhabit, and immerse ourselves in nature's tranquil embrace.

In its timeless wisdom, the forest invites us to partake in a journey of rejuvenation and self-discovery. It invites us to tread softly upon its moss-carpeted floor, to breathe in the crisp, clean air infused with the scent of pine and damp earth, to listen to the symphony of bird songs and rustling leaves, and to let our gaze wander over the myriad shades of green that paint its vast canvas.

This whispered invitation is not merely a call to explore the physical realm of the forest. It is an invitation to delve into the depths of our being, reconnect with our roots, and rediscover the profound peace within us. It is an invitation to experience 'forest bathing,' a practice that has the power to heal, soothe, and transform.

As you turn the pages of this book, you will find yourself walking along the forest's winding paths, feeling the cool shade of its towering trees and basking in the dappled sunlight that filters through its dense canopy. You will learn to listen to the forest's whispered invitation and to respond to it with an open heart and a tranquil mind. You will learn to embrace the forest's embrace, and in doing so, you will embark on a journey that will lead you to a place of serenity, balance, and profound inner peace.

The Enchanting Dance of Light and Shadow

As you step into the forest, the world outside begins to fade, replaced by a symphony of sounds that is the forest's own. The rustling leaves, the whispering wind, and the distant call of a bird all merge into a harmonious melody that seems to resonate with your soul. But it is not just the sounds that captivate you. It is the enchanting dance of light and shadow that truly draws you in.

Imagine standing at the edge of a forest at dawn, the world still hushed in the soft embrace of twilight. As the first rays of the sun pierce the veil of darkness, they illuminate the forest in a breathtaking spectacle. The light filters through the canopy, casting dappled shadows that dance and sway with the gentle rustling of the leaves. It's a mesmerizing ballet of light and shadow, a spectacle that changes with each passing moment, each shifting leaf, each fluttering bird.

This dance is not merely a visual feast. It is an invitation, a beckoning from the forest itself. It invites you to step into its verdant heart, lose yourself in its tranquil depths, and become one with its rhythmic pulse. It is an invitation to experience forest bathing, immerse yourself in the forest's embrace, let its serene beauty wash over you, and rejuvenate your spirit.

You feel a sense of peace as you watch the enchanting dance of light and shadow. With its noise and chaos, the world outside seems distant, almost unreal. All that exists is the forest, its soothing rhythm, and its gentle whisper that seems to say, "Come, step into my heart. Let me show you a world of tranquility and beauty where you can find your rhythm and peace."

This is the magic of forest bathing. It is not just about walking in a forest. It is about immersing yourself in its embrace, letting its tranquility seep into your soul, and finding a sense of peace and rejuvenation that is as enchanting as the dance of light and shadow. It is about embracing the forest's embrace, about becoming one with its verdant heart. This book is your guide on this journey, a pathway to serenity that begins with the enchanting dance of light and shadow.

A Pathway to Serenity: Your Journey Begins Here

There lies a pathway to serenity in the gentle rustle of leaves, in the soft murmur of a brook, in the hushed whispers of the wind. This book, dear reader, is your guide to discovering that path, your compass to navigate the verdant labyrinth of tranquility that is forest bathing.

The purpose of this book is not merely to introduce you to the concept of forest bathing but to invite you into a world where the boundaries between self and nature blur, where the heart beats in rhythm with the earth's pulse. It is a journey of self-discovery, of finding peace in the embrace of the forest, of learning to listen to the silent songs of nature.

The goals of this book are manifold. It aims to guide you, step by step, into the heart of the forest, to teach you to see not just with your eyes but with your soul. It seeks to help you find a sanctuary amidst the trees, where you can shed the weight of the world and clothe yourself in tranquility. It aspires to show you how to tap into nature's healing power, bathe in the forest's refreshing energy, and rejuvenate your spirit in the cool, green shade of the woods.

This book is your journey, which begins here, in the embrace of the forest. It is a journey that will take you deep into the heart of nature, where you will find serenity and a deeper understanding of yourself and your place in the world. It is a journey that will change you and leave you refreshed, revitalized, and renewed.

So, dear reader, take a deep breath. Feel the cool, fresh air fills your lungs, taste the sweetness of the forest on your tongue. Listen to the forest's whispered invitation. Your journey begins here. Welcome to the pathway to serenity. Welcome to the world of forest bathing.

A Glimpse into the Verdant Heart of the Forest

As we embark on this journey together, we will delve into the verdant heart of the forest, where tranquility reigns, and the hustle and bustle of the world fades into a distant murmur. This book is not merely a guide but a companion, a gentle hand leading you into the embrace of the forest, where you will learn to commune with nature in a way that rejuvenates your spirit and soothes your soul.

We will begin by exploring the concept of forest bathing, a practice that originated in Japan, known as Shinrin-Yoku. This is not a physical bath but rather an immersion of the senses, a bathing in the forest's atmosphere. We will delve into the science behind it, understanding how this simple act of being in nature can profoundly affect our health and well-being.

From there, we will journey through the seasons, experiencing the forest in its many moods. We will learn to appreciate the delicate lacework of frost on a winter's morning, the vibrant explosion of spring blossoms, the dappled sunlight of a summer's day, and the fiery palette of autumn leaves. Each season brings unique gifts; we will learn to receive them with open hearts.

We will also explore the forest at different times of day, from dawn's peaceful stillness to twilight's mysterious depths. We will learn to listen to the forest's symphony, the rustle of leaves, the song of birds, the whisper of the wind. We will learn to see not just with our eyes but with our hearts, discovering the hidden beauty that lies beneath the surface.

Finally, we will learn practical techniques for forest bathing, from mindful walking to deep breathing exercises. These techniques will help you to fully immerse yourself in the forest's embrace, allowing you to tap into its healing power.

This journey is not about reaching a destination but about savoring the journey itself. It is about learning to slow down, be present, and connect with the natural world in a way that nourishes our spirit. So, let us step into the verdant heart of the forest and let its soothing whispers guide us on our path to serenity.

1

THE ORIGIN AND HISTORY OF FOREST BATHING

In the tranquility of the dawn, when the world is still half-asleep, the forest awakens. The leaves rustle gently, whispering secrets to the wind. The crisp and fresh air carries the scent of damp earth and the subtle perfume of wildflowers. In its serene majesty, the forest invites you to step into its embrace, lose yourself in its verdant labyrinth, and find solace in its tranquil bosom. This is the essence of forest bathing, a practice as old as the forest itself yet as refreshing as the morning dew.

Forest bathing, or Shinrin-Yoku as it is known in Japan, is not merely a walk in the woods. It is a mindful immersion in the forest atmosphere, a deliberate act of connecting with nature on a deep, sensory level. It is about allowing the forest to seep into your being, to cleanse your mind, and to rejuvenate your spirit.

The genesis of forest bathing is as timeless as the forest itself. It is rooted in the primal relationship between humans and nature, nurtured by countless generations across diverse cultures and vast landscapes. It is a relationship that has evolved, adapted, and flourished, much like the forest itself.

The concept of forest bathing is not a new one. It is an ancient practice, a forgotten wisdom that has been rediscovered in our modern world. It is a testament to the enduring allure of the forest, a testament to the healing power of nature.

The forest has always been a sanctuary, a place of refuge and renewal. It has been a source of inspiration, insight, strength, and serenity. It has been a teacher, a healer, a guide. It has been a companion, a confidant, a friend.

In its infinite wisdom, the forest has always known the secret to a balanced and harmonious life. It has always known the art of being, the art of living, the art of forest bathing. And now, it invites us to partake in this ancient wisdom, to embark on a journey of self-discovery and self-healing, to immerse ourselves in the tranquil beauty of the forest, and to bathe in its restorative embrace.

As we delve deeper into the origins and history of forest bathing, we will explore its ancient roots, Japanese influence, scientific validation, global spread, and modern adaptations. We will journey through time and space, through cultures and continents, through science and spirituality. We will journey into the heart of the forest, into the heart of forest bathing. And in doing so, we will journey into the heart of ourselves.

Ancient Roots: Forest Bathing in Early Cultures

In the hushed whispers of the past, where time was measured by the sun's journey across the sky and the changing of the seasons, our ancestors found solace and sustenance in the embrace of the forest. Though not named as such, the concept of forest bathing was deeply ingrained in their lives. It was a time when humanity was intricately woven into the fabric of nature when the forest was not just a resource but a sanctuary, a healer, and a teacher.

The ancient cultures, from the Celts of Europe to the indigenous tribes of the Americas, from the sages of India to the shamans of Siberia, all revered the forest. They recognized its power, its wisdom, and its ability to heal. They bathed in its beauty, sounds, scents, and silence, absorbing its essence into their very being. This was their form of forest bathing, a practice born out of necessity and reverence and as natural as breathing.

In these early cultures, the forest was a sacred space. It was a place of worship, a place of learning, a place of healing. The Celts, for instance, believed in the spiritual presence of trees, each species possessing unique wisdom and energy. They would retreat into the forest for meditation, healing, and guidance. The indigenous tribes of the Americas, too, held a deep respect for the forest. They saw it as a living entity, a provider, a protector. They would immerse themselves in its depths, seeking wisdom, peace, and connection.

In the East, the sages of ancient India found enlightenment under the Bodhi tree, while the monks of China sought solace in the bamboo groves. The forest was their sanctuary, source of inspiration, and pathway to spiritual awakening. They bathed in the forest's tranquility, energy, wisdom, absorbing essence, spirit, and life force.

Though varied in their rituals and beliefs, these ancient practices shared a common thread - the profound understanding of the healing power of the forest. They recognized that the forest was more than just a collection of trees. It was a living, breathing entity, a source of life, a source of healing, a source of wisdom. They understood that by immersing themselves in the forest and bathing in its beauty, energy, and silence, they could find peace and healing and rediscover themselves.

As we journey through history, we find that the essence of forest bathing has remained unchanged. It is a practice that transcends cultures and time. It is a practice that speaks to the very core of our being, reminds us of our deep-rooted connection with nature, and invites us to return to our origins.

The Japanese Influence: Shinrin-Yoku

In the heart of the Land of the Rising Sun, a practice was born that would soon ripple out across the globe, touching lives with its gentle, healing touch. This practice, known as Shinrin-Yoku, or forest bathing, is a cornerstone of Japanese culture and has profoundly influenced the world's understanding and appreciation of nature's therapeutic potential.

Shinrin-Yoku, when translated, means 'taking in the forest atmosphere' or 'forest bathing.' It was developed in Japan during the 1980s to respond to the increasing stress and health issues associated with urban living. The Japanese government, recognizing the need for a healthier, more balanced lifestyle, introduced Shinrin-Yoku as a form of ecotherapy, encouraging citizens to immerse themselves in the tranquil beauty of the country's lush forests.

The practice is deceptively simple yet profoundly impactful. It involves walking slowly, almost meditatively, through a forested area, breathing deeply, and allowing the senses to fully engage with the surrounding nature. The aim is not to reach a destination but to soak in the journey, to bathe in the forest's atmosphere, and to emerge rejuvenated and at peace.

The impact of Shinrin-Yoku on Japanese society was transformative. It not only improved physical health but also fostered a deeper connection with nature, promoting mental and emotional well-being. The practice became a bridge, linking the modern, fast-paced world with the timeless wisdom and tranquility of the forest.

The influence of Shinrin-Yoku did not stop at Japan's borders. The practice resonated with people worldwide, leading to a global renaissance of forest bathing. Different cultures have embraced the Japanese concept of Shinrin-Yoku, each adding unique interpretations and adaptations, yet united by the shared understanding of the forest's healing power.

The impact of Shinrin-Yoku is a testament to the universal human need for connection with nature. It serves as a reminder that amidst the hustle and bustle of modern life, the forest remains a sanctuary, a place of tranquility and rejuvenation, waiting to welcome us into its soothing embrace.

The Science Behind Forest Bathing

In the stillness of the forest, where the air is filled with the scent of pine and the rustling of leaves, a profound sense of healing transcends the physical realm. This is the essence of forest bathing, a practice deeply rooted in various cultures for centuries. But what is the science behind this seemingly mystical experience? Let us delve into the historical perspective of the science behind forest bathing.

The scientific exploration of forest bathing began in earnest in the 1980s in Japan, where the practice is known as Shinrin-Yoku. The Japanese government, recognizing the potential health benefits of spending time in nature, initiated a series of studies investigating the physiological effects of forest bathing. The results were nothing short of remarkable.

Researchers discovered that immersion in the forest environment could reduce blood pressure, lower cortisol levels, and improve concentration and memory. They also found that forest bathing could boost the immune system by increasing the activity of natural killer cells, a type of white blood cell that fights off viruses and cancer.

The key to these benefits, they found, lies in the natural compounds released by trees, known as phytoncides. These organic compounds, which trees emit to protect themselves from insects and decay, significantly impact human health. When inhaled, phytoncides have been shown to enhance human immune function and reduce stress hormones.

As the scientific understanding of forest bathing deepened, the practice began to gain recognition beyond Japan. Researchers worldwide started to explore nature's therapeutic effects, leading to the emergence of a new field of study known as ecotherapy.

In the 21st century, the science of forest bathing continues to evolve. Modern studies are exploring the impact of forest bathing on mental health, with promising results indicating that time spent in nature can alleviate symptoms of depression and anxiety.

The science behind forest bathing, while still a growing field, offers a compelling testament to the healing power of nature. It is a gentle reminder that the forest remains a sanctuary of tranquility and wellness in our increasingly urbanized and digital world. As we continue to explore the depths of the forest's healing potential, we are also rediscovering our innate connection to the natural world. This connection can rejuvenate our bodies, refresh our minds, and restore our spirits.

Forest Bathing Across Continents

As the sun began to rise over the horizon, painting the sky with hues of pink and orange, the concept of forest bathing, too, began to awaken and stretch its roots beyond the borders of Japan. The world was about to experience a gentle revolution, a quiet transformation that would change how we perceive and interact with nature.

The 1980s marked the beginning of this global journey. The whispers of the forest began to echo in the hearts of people across continents, from the lush greenery of Europe to the vast wilderness of North America, from the dense jungles of South America to the unique biodiversity of Australia. The concept of forest bathing was no longer confined to the Land of the Rising Sun; it was now a global phenomenon, a universal call to return to nature.

In Europe, the idea of forest bathing resonated deeply with the people. With its rich history and diverse landscapes, the continent embraced the practice with open arms. The lush forests of Scandinavia, the enchanting woods of Germany, and the tranquil groves of the United Kingdom all became sanctuaries for those seeking solace and healing in nature. Forest bathing clubs began to sprout, offering guided walks and promoting the benefits of this mindful practice.

Across the Atlantic, North America, too, was captivated by the allure of forest bathing. The vast wilderness of Canada and the United States, with their towering pines, majestic oaks, and serene lakes, provided the perfect backdrop for the practice. The concept was introduced in various wellness programs, retreats, and corporate environments, encouraging people to disconnect from their hectic lives and reconnect with nature.

In South America, forest bathing found a unique expression. The indigenous communities, with their deep-rooted connection to the land, integrated the practice into their daily lives, blending it seamlessly with their ancient traditions. With its unparalleled biodiversity, the Amazon rainforest became a haven for forest bathers, offering an immersive experience like no other.

Down under in Australia, the practice took on a different hue. The continent's unique flora and fauna added a distinct flavor to forest bathing. The eucalyptus forests, with their soothing aroma and the melodious calls of native birds, created a healing and rejuvenating environment.

As we trace the forest bathing journey across continents, we see a common thread - a universal longing for a deeper connection with nature. Despite our diverse cultures and landscapes, we are all drawn to the tranquility of the forest, the gentle whisper of the leaves, and the soothing rhythm of nature's heartbeat. This global spread of forest bathing is a testament to our shared love for nature, a reminder of our inherent need to be in harmony with the world.

Forest Bathing in the 21st Century

As the dawn of the 21st century broke, the world was in the throes of a technological revolution. The rapid pace of life, the constant connectivity, and the ceaseless hum of digital devices began to take a toll on the collective human spirit. Amidst this whirlwind of progress, an ancient practice began to re-emerge, offering a soothing balm to the frazzled nerves of modern society. This practice was forest bathing, a concept that had its roots in the tranquil woods and serene landscapes of our ancestors.

In the 21st century, forest bathing has been adapted and embraced in a myriad of ways across the globe. It has transcended cultural boundaries and been integrated into modern life's fabric, offering a gentle reminder of our inherent connection to the natural world.

In urban environments, where concrete jungles often replace green forests, city dwellers have found innovative ways to engage in forest bathing. Urban parks and green spaces have become sanctuaries, offering a slice of nature amidst the steel and glass structures. These spaces, though smaller and more contained than sprawling forests, still allow individuals to immerse themselves in nature, breathe deeply, and find a moment of tranquility in the chaos of city life.

In healthcare, forest bathing has been recognized for its therapeutic benefits. Medical professionals and therapists have begun incorporating forest bathing into treatment plans, acknowledging the healing power of nature. Hospitals and healthcare facilities have started to design healing gardens, spaces where patients can engage in forest bathing, promoting recovery and well-being.

In education, schools and universities have started to recognize the value of forest bathing. Outdoor classrooms and nature-based learning experiences are being integrated into curriculums, fostering a love for nature in younger generations and promoting the practice of forest bathing.

In the business world, companies have begun to understand the importance of employee well-being and the role of nature in promoting productivity. Corporate retreats often include forest bathing experiences, allowing employees to disconnect from their screens and reconnect with the natural world.

As we navigate the complexities of the 21st century, the practice of forest bathing serves as a beacon, guiding us back to our roots and the simplicity and serenity of the natural world. It is a practice adapted and adopted by modern society, a testament to its timeless appeal and enduring relevance. As we move forward, it is clear that forest bathing will continue to play a crucial role in our lives, offering a sanctuary of tranquility in an ever-evolving world.

Reflecting on the Journey of Forest Bathing

As we draw the curtain on this exploration of forest bathing, we find ourselves standing at the edge of a green expanse, the whispers of the trees echoing the wisdom of centuries. From its ancient roots to modern adaptations, the forest bathing journey is a testament to the enduring bond between humans and nature. This bond has been nurtured and cherished across cultures and continents.

The genesis of forest bathing is as old as humanity itself. It is a practice born out of an intuitive understanding of the healing power of nature, an understanding that our earliest ancestors shared. They sought solace in the embrace of the forest, finding a balm for their weary souls in its serenity. This ancient wisdom passed down through generations, has been the bedrock upon which the practice of forest bathing stands.

The influence of the Japanese practice of Shinrin-Yoku has been instrumental in shaping the modern understanding of forest bathing. It has brought to the fore the therapeutic benefits of immersing oneself in the forest, of letting the symphony of nature envelop the senses. While still in its nascent stages, the science behind forest bathing has lent credence to what our ancestors instinctively knew - that the forest is a sanctuary of healing and rejuvenation.

The global spread of forest bathing reflects our collective yearning for a return to nature, a yearning that has been amplified in the face of the relentless pace of modern life. Across continents, people seek refuge in the forest, finding in its dappled light and rustling leaves a respite from the world's clamor.

The 21st century has seen a resurgence of interest in forest bathing, with modern adaptations making it accessible to a broader audience. From guided forest therapy walks to forest bathing retreats, the practice has evolved to meet the needs of a society increasingly disconnected from nature.

As we reflect on the forest bathing journey, we are reminded of the timeless wisdom of the forest. It is a wisdom that speaks of balance, harmony, and the interconnectedness of all life. It is a wisdom that invites us to step into the forest, to bathe in its tranquility, and to emerge rejuvenated, with a renewed sense of our place in the natural world. The journey of forest bathing is, in essence, a journey towards rediscovering our innate connection with nature, a journey that is as enriching as it is enlightening.

Chapter Summary

- Forest bathing, or Shinrin-Yoku, is rooted in the primal relationship between humans and nature. It involves a mindful immersion in the forest atmosphere, allowing the forest to cleanse the mind and rejuvenate the spirit.
- The concept of forest bathing is not new. It has been practiced by ancient cultures across the globe, from the Celts of Europe to the indigenous tribes of the Americas, who revered the forest as a sacred space and a source of wisdom and healing.
- The practice of Shinrin-Yoku was developed in Japan during the 1980s as a form of ecotherapy. It had a transformative impact on Japanese society, improving physical health and fostering a deeper connection with nature.
- The science behind forest bathing began to be explored in the 1980s. Studies found that immersion in the forest environment could reduce blood pressure, lower cortisol levels, and improve concentration and memory. The key to these benefits lies in the natural compounds trees release, known as phytoncides.
- The concept of forest bathing has spread globally, resonating with people worldwide. Different cultures have embraced it, each adding unique interpretations and adaptations, yet united by the shared understanding of the forest's healing power.
- In the 21st century, forest bathing has been adapted and embraced in various ways globally. It has been integrated into urban environments, healthcare, education, and business, reassuring us of our inherent connection to the natural world.
- The global spread of forest bathing is a testament to our shared love for nature and our inherent need to be in harmony with the world. Despite our diverse cultures and landscapes, we are all drawn to the tranquility of the forest.

- The journey of forest bathing, from its ancient roots to its modern adaptations, is a testament to the enduring bond between humans and nature. It serves as a beacon, guiding us back to our roots and the simplicity and serenity of the natural world.

2

THE SCIENCE BEHIND FOREST BATHING

In the stillness of the forest, where the air is filled with the gentle rustling of leaves and the distant melody of birdsong, a profound connection is forged between us and the natural world. This connection, as ancient as our species itself, is the essence of forest bathing, a practice that invites us to immerse ourselves in the serene beauty of the woods. But what is it about this simple act that has such a profound impact on our well-being? What is the science behind the tranquility and rejuvenation we experience when we surrender ourselves to the forest's embrace?

Forest bathing, or Shinrin-yoku, is not merely a walk in the woods. It is a mindful immersion, a slow, deliberate journey into the heart of the forest. It is about letting the forest in, allowing it to fill our senses, touch our souls, and heal our bodies. It is about being present, aware, and one with the natural world.

The mysteries of forest bathing lie not just in the ethereal beauty of the forest but also in the intricate dance of biology, psychology, and chemistry that unfolds within us as we step into the woodland realm. This chapter will delve into the science behind forest bathing, exploring how our bodies react to the forest, the psychological impact of this practice, the healing power of phytoncides - nature's own medicine, and the role of our senses in engaging with the forest.

We will also take a global perspective, examining scientific studies worldwide that shed light on the myriad benefits of forest bathing. As we journey through this chapter, we will unravel the mysteries of forest bathing, revealing the science that underpins this soulful practice.

In the end, we hope to deepen your understanding and appreciation of forest bathing, encouraging you to embrace both the science and the soul of this rejuvenating practice. For in the heart of the forest, we find not just tranquility and wellness but also a profound connection to the very essence of life itself.

The Biological Response: How Our Bodies React to the Forest

As we step into the forest, leaving behind the concrete jungle and the rush of urban life, our bodies begin to respond to the serene embrace of nature in ways more profound than we often realize. This section delves into the fascinating biological response that occurs when we immerse ourselves in the forest, a phenomenon that forms the very foundation of forest bathing.

The moment our feet touch the soft, moss-covered forest floor, our heart rate begins to slow down, matching the tranquil rhythm of the forest. The air, rich with the scent of earth and foliage, fills our lungs, purifying them with each breath. This is not merely a poetic sentiment but a scientifically observed fact. Studies have shown that forest environments can significantly reduce blood pressure and heart rate, promoting relaxation and calm.

As we venture deeper into the forest, our bodies continue to respond to the forest's subtle cues. The gentle rustling of leaves, the distant call of a bird, the whisper of a breeze; these sounds, often drowned out in our daily lives, come alive in the forest. They act as gentle stimuli, engaging our auditory senses in a soothing symphony of natural sounds. This auditory engagement has been linked to a decrease in stress hormones, further enhancing the calming effect of the forest.

The forest air, imbued with natural compounds known as phytoncides, plays a crucial role in our biological response. These compounds, released by trees and plants, have been found to boost our immune system. As we breathe in the forest air, we inhale these phytoncides, which increase the activity of natural killer cells in our bodies, enhancing our overall immunity.

The forest's visual spectacle, a tapestry of greens, browns, and myriad hues, captivates our sight, providing a feast for our eyes. This visual engagement is not merely aesthetic; it profoundly impacts our mental well-being. The color green, predominant in forest environments, has been associated with feelings of relaxation and calmness, contributing to the overall therapeutic effect of forest bathing.

In essence, our bodies react to the forest in a symphony of responses, each note contributing to a state of relaxation, rejuvenation, and healing. This biological response, deeply ingrained in our evolutionary history, is a testament to our intrinsic connection with nature, a bond that forest bathing allows us to rediscover and strengthen.

The Psychological Impact: Forest Bathing and the Mind

A profound transformation begins in the heart of the forest, where the air is rich with the scent of pine and the rustle of leaves. As we step away from the clamor of the urban world and immerse ourselves in the tranquil embrace of nature, our minds begin to respond in ways that are as profound as they are healing. This section delves into the psychological impact of forest bathing, exploring how this simple yet powerful practice can soothe our minds, uplift our spirits, and rekindle our connection with the natural world.

The forest, with its verdant canopy and dappled sunlight, is a sanctuary for the mind. As we wander its paths, our thoughts begin to slow, mirroring the unhurried rhythm of the natural world. The constant barrage of stimuli that characterizes our modern lives fades away, replaced by the gentle symphony of the forest. This reduction in sensory overload allows our minds to relax, reducing stress and promoting a state of peaceful mindfulness.

Forest bathing also has a profound impact on our mood. The beauty of the natural world, with its intricate patterns and vibrant colors, can evoke feelings of awe and wonder that elevate our spirits and foster a sense of well-being. Moreover, being present in the forest, truly seeing, hearing, and feeling the world around us, can help ground us in the moment, alleviating anxiety and promoting a sense of calm.

The forest is not just a place of beauty but also a source of healing. Studies have shown that spending time in nature can boost levels of serotonin, the 'feel good' neurotransmitter, and reduce levels of cortisol, the 'stress hormone.' This can improve mood, sleep quality, and overall mental health.

Moreover, the forest can serve as a catalyst for introspection and personal growth. As we walk among the trees, we are reminded of the cycles of growth and decay, of the interconnectedness of all life. These reflections can foster a sense of perspective, helping us navigate challenges with greater resilience and grace.

In conclusion, the psychological impact of forest bathing is as diverse as it is profound. This practice offers many benefits for our minds, from reducing stress and improving mood to fostering mindfulness and promoting personal growth. As we continue to explore the science behind forest bathing, we come to understand that the forest is not just a place of beauty but a sanctuary for the soul, a place where we can reconnect with ourselves and the world around us in the most profound of ways.

The Healing Power of Phytoncides: Nature's Own Medicine

In the heart of the forest, a silent symphony of healing unfolds. It is a performance conducted by trees, a concert of invisible compounds known as phytoncides. These are volatile organic compounds, a natural elixir exuded by trees and plants, and a kind of botanical balm that permeates the forest air.

Phytoncides are not merely the scent of the forest; they are the forest's own medicine, a testament to the healing power of nature. They are the trees' defense mechanism against harmful insects and bacteria, but they serve a different purpose for us humans. They are a balm for our bodies, a salve for our souls, a tonic that can help to restore our health and well-being.

When we breathe in the forest air, we are inhaling these phytoncides. They enter our bodies, and their healing power begins to work its magic. Scientific studies have shown that exposure to phytoncides can boost our immune system, increasing the activity of our natural killer cells, the body's first line of defense against viruses and cancer.

Phytoncides also have a calming effect on our bodies. They can lower our blood pressure, reduce our heart rate, and decrease our levels of the stress hormone cortisol. They can help improve our mood, reduce anxiety, and promote peace and well-being.

The forest is not just a place of beauty and tranquility. It is a living, breathing pharmacy, a natural health spa that offers us a unique form of therapy. It is a place where we can immerse ourselves in the healing power of nature, where we can breathe in the forest's medicine and let it soothe our bodies and minds.

So, take a deep breath the next time you step into a forest. Breathe in the scent of the trees, the earth's fragrance, and the forest air's aroma. Know that you are breathing in phytoncides, nature's own medicine, and let their healing power wash over you. Let the forest bathe you in its healing light, cleanse your body and mind, and restore your health and spirit.

This is the science and the soul of forest bathing, a deep dive into the healing power of nature, a journey into the heart of the forest, a voyage of discovery and healing. It is a journey that can transform your life and bring you peace, health, and well-being. It is a journey that begins with a single step, a single breath, and a single moment in the heart of the forest.

The Role of the Senses: Engaging with the Forest

In the heart of the forest, where the air is pure, and the silence is only broken by the rustling of leaves or the distant call of a bird, our senses awaken in a profound and subtle way. In its tranquil majesty, the forest invites us to engage with it, not merely as passive observers but as active participants in a sensory symphony as old as life itself.

Often dulled by the monotony of urban life, our senses find a new vitality in the forest. The eyes, accustomed to the harsh glare of artificial lights, are soothed by the gentle play of sunlight filtering through the canopy of leaves. The myriad shades of green, the intricate patterns of bark, and the delicate beauty of a single leaf - all offer a visual feast that is both calming and refreshing.

The sense of smell, too, is awakened in the forest. The earthy scent of the soil, the fresh fragrance of pine needles, and the subtle perfume of wildflowers mingle in the air to create a natural, healing, and rejuvenating aromatherapy. This is not merely a poetic notion but a scientific fact. The forest air is rich in phytoncides, which have been proven to boost our immune system and enhance our well-being.

The forest also offers a symphony of sounds that is deeply soothing. The whispering of the wind through the leaves, the gentle rustling of small creatures in the undergrowth, and the melodic songs of birds create a natural white noise known to reduce stress and promote relaxation.

The sense of touch, too, is engaged in the forest. The rough texture of bark, the softness of moss, the coolness of a stream - these tactile experiences connect us directly with the natural world, grounding us in the present moment and fostering a sense of peace and well-being.

Finally, the forest engages our sense of taste. The tangy taste of wild berries, the sweetness of sap, the freshness of spring water - these natural flavors remind us of our deep connection with the earth and its bounty.

Engaging with the forest through our senses is not merely a pleasant experience but a powerful healing practice. It is a way of immersing ourselves in the natural world, reconnecting with our roots, and finding peace and rejuvenation in the heart of nature. It is, in essence, the soul of forest bathing.

Scientific Studies from Around the World

As we delve deeper into the verdant heart of forest bathing, it is essential to broaden our perspective and explore the global scientific studies that have been conducted on this subject. In its vastness and diversity, the world has embraced the healing power of the forest, and science has been the compass guiding this journey.

Numerous studies have been conducted in the land of the rising sun, Japan, where the practice of Shinrin-yoku, or forest bathing, was born. Researchers from the Nippon Medical School in Tokyo discovered that forest bathing significantly increases the activity of natural killer cells, an immune system component that fights cancer. This effect was found to last for more than 30 days after the forest visit, painting a picture of enduring health benefits that linger long after one has left the forest's embrace.

Across the Pacific, in the United States, a study by the University of Illinois revealed that residents with more green space in their environment reported lower stress levels and higher life satisfaction. This study, among others, underscores the profound impact of nature on our mental well-being.

In Europe, a study conducted in the Netherlands found that people who spent more time in green spaces had lower rates of depression and anxiety. Similarly, researchers in the United Kingdom found that being in nature, even briefly, improves mood, reduces feelings of stress or anger, and enhances physical well-being.

Venturing further to South Korea, a country that has established healing forests, a study found that forest bathing trips significantly reduced the scores for anxiety, depression, anger, fatigue, and confusion while improving vigor scores among participants.

These studies, scattered across the globe, are like the many trees of a forest. Each one stands tall, contributing to a more significant understanding, a global perspective that forest bathing is not merely a leisurely walk in the woods but a potent tool for health and healing.

As we conclude this section, let us remember that the science of forest bathing is as diverse and interconnected as the world's forests themselves. From the sun-dappled cedar forests of Japan to the towering redwoods of America, the whispering pines of Europe to the healing forests of Korea, each holds a piece of the puzzle, a unique contribution to our understanding of this remarkable practice. Let us sit quietly with the knowledge we have gained, like a forest bather beneath the trees, absorbing the world's wisdom.

Embracing the Science and Soul of Forest Bathing

As we close this chapter, we find ourselves standing at the edge of a vast expanse, the forest of knowledge we have traversed together. We have delved into the science behind forest bathing, unraveling the intricate tapestry of biological responses, psychological impacts, and the healing power of phytoncides. We have engaged our senses and explored the global perspective, gathering insights from scientific studies worldwide. Now, it is time to step back, breathe in the cool, crisp air, and embrace the science and soul of forest bathing.

In all its lush complexity, the forest is not merely a backdrop to our lives but an active participant in our well-being. It is a living, breathing entity that interacts with us deeply and profoundly. The science we have explored illuminates this relationship, shedding light on the myriad ways the forest nurtures, heals, and brings us back to ourselves.

As we have discovered, our bodies are finely tuned to respond to the forest. The rustle of leaves, the scent of pine, the dappled sunlight filtering through the canopy - these are not just sensory experiences but triggers for a cascade of biological reactions. They lower our blood pressure, boost our immune system, and flood our bodies with calm and well-being.

Our minds, too, are deeply affected by the forest. The quiet solitude the gentle rhythm of nature, the sense of being part of something larger than ourselves - these experiences soothe our frazzled nerves, quiet our racing thoughts, and help us regain our mental equilibrium.

And then there are the phytoncides, those invisible, aromatic compounds that trees release into the air. They are nature's own medicine, working their subtle magic on us, strengthening our bodies, and fortifying our spirits.

But the science, as illuminating as it is, only tells part of the story. The soul of forest bathing lies in the experience itself - in the quiet moments of connection, the sense of awe and wonder, and the deep, abiding peace that settles over us as we immerse ourselves in the forest.

So, as we step out of the forest of knowledge and back into the world, let us carry with us the science and the soul of forest bathing. Let us remember that the forest is not just a place but a state of being, a way of connecting with the world and ourselves. Let us embrace the forest and, in doing so, embrace our own well-being. For in the end, the science and soul of forest bathing are the same - a testament to the profound, healing power of nature.

Chapter Summary

- Forest bathing is a mindful immersion into the forest, allowing it to fill our senses and heal our bodies. It is about being present and aware, fostering a deep connection with the natural world.
- Our bodies react to the forest in a symphony of responses, including a reduction in heart rate and blood pressure, a decrease in stress hormones, and an enhancement of our immune system through inhaling phytoncides.
- Forest bathing has a profound psychological impact, reducing stress, improving mood, fostering mindfulness, and promoting personal growth. It serves as a sanctuary for the mind, allowing for introspection and a sense of calm.

- Phytoncides, volatile organic compounds released by trees, play a crucial role in our biological response to the forest. They boost our immune system, lower our blood pressure, reduce our heart rate, and decrease our levels of the stress hormone cortisol.
- Engaging with the forest through our senses is a powerful healing practice. The forest offers a sensory symphony that is both calming and invigorating, grounding us in the present moment and fostering a sense of peace and well-being.
- Scientific studies worldwide have shed light on the myriad benefits of forest bathing, including increased activity of natural killer cells, reduced stress levels, higher life satisfaction, lower rates of depression and anxiety, and improved mood and vigor.
- The science of forest bathing is as diverse and interconnected as the world's forests themselves. Each forest, from the cedar forests of Japan to the redwoods of America, contributes to our understanding of this remarkable practice.
- The science and soul of forest bathing are the same - a testament to nature's profound healing power. The forest is not just a place but a state of being, a way of connecting with the world and ourselves.

3

THE ART OF MINDFUL WALKING: YOUR FIRST STEPS

We begin our journey in the forest's heart, where the air is a symphony of subtle fragrances, and the light filters through the leaves in a dance of shadows and sunbeams. This is not a journey of miles and landmarks but one of awareness, presence, and being in the moment. This is the journey of mindful walking.

Mindful walking is an art that invites us to slow down, step away from the rush and clamor of our daily lives, and immerse ourselves in the tranquil embrace of nature. It is a dance with the forest, a gentle waltz where we move in harmony with the natural world's rhythm.

As we embark on this journey, we leave behind our worries, distractions, and preoccupations. We approach the forest with an open heart, ready to receive its wisdom. We are not merely observers but active participants in the forest's life. We are part of the forest, and the forest is part of us.

The journey of mindful walking is a journey of discovery. With each step, we uncover the secrets of the forest. We learn to see the beauty in the smallest leaf, to hear the music in the softest breeze, and to feel the life pulsating in the ground beneath our feet. We learn to see the world with new eyes, hear with new ears, and feel with a new heart.

Embracing the journey of mindful walking is embracing a new way of being, a new way of experiencing the world. It is a journey that can transform and bring us peace, joy, and a deep connection with the natural world. It is a journey that begins with a single step, a step taken with awareness, intention, and love.

So, let us begin. Let us step into the forest, into the heart of nature. Let us embrace the journey of mindful walking, and let the forest guide, heal, and awaken us to the beauty and wonder of the world around us.

The Rhythm of Nature: Tuning into the Forest's Heartbeat

As you stand on the threshold of the forest, take a moment to close your eyes and tune into the rhythm of nature. It is a rhythm that is both ancient and ever-present, a rhythm that pulses with life and vibrates with the universe's energy. It is the forest's heartbeat and is waiting for you to join its dance.

The rhythm of nature cannot be heard with the ears, but rather, it must be felt with the heart. It is a subtle, gentle pulse that resonates within the deepest parts of your being, a rhythm that is as much a part of you as your heartbeat. It is a rhythm that speaks of the interconnectedness of all life, the delicate balance between all living things, and the profound beauty that can be found in every moment.

To tune into the forest's heartbeat, you must first quiet your mind and open your senses. Let go of your thoughts, your worries, and your expectations. Allow your breath to slow and your body to relax. Feel the earth beneath your feet, the air on your skin, the sun's warmth, and the shade's coolness. Listen to the rustling of the leaves, the chirping of the birds, the whispering of the wind, and the silence beneath it all.

As you immerse yourself in the forest, you will begin to feel a rhythm, a pulse, a heartbeat. It may be faint initially, but it will grow stronger and more apparent as you walk mindfully. This is the rhythm of the forest, the rhythm of life itself. It is a rhythm that invites you to move in harmony with it, dance with it, and become one with it.

Tuning into the forest's heartbeat is not just about listening but also about feeling, connecting, and becoming one with nature's rhythm. It is about allowing the forest to guide, teach, and heal you. It is about surrendering to the moment, beauty, and magic in the forest.

So, take a deep breath, take that first step, and let the rhythm of the forest guide you on your journey of mindful walking. Let it lead you into tranquility, immersion, and rejuvenation. Let it awaken a sense of wonder, awe, and gratitude within you. Let it remind you of the simple joy of being alive and part of this beautiful, interconnected web of life.

And as you walk, remember: you are not just walking in the forest; you are walking with the forest, dancing to the rhythm of its heartbeat, becoming one with the rhythm of nature.

The First Step: Initiating the Dance with Nature

The first step into the forest is a moment of profound significance. It is the initiation of a dance with nature that is as old as the earth itself. As you cross the threshold from the manufactured world into the realm of the wild, you are not merely a spectator but an active participant in the grand ballet of life.

Imagine standing at the forest's edge, your feet firmly planted on the ground, your heart beating in rhythm with the earth's pulse. The air is cool and fresh, carrying the scent of damp earth and the subtle perfume of wildflowers. The trees stand tall and majestic, their leaves rustling softly in the breeze, whispering secrets of the forest. The sunlight filters through the canopy, casting dappled shadows on the forest floor. It is a scene of tranquil beauty, a symphony of sights, sounds, and scents that invites you to step in and join the dance.

As you take your first step, feel the texture of the earth beneath your feet. It may be soft, mossy, or rough and pebbled, but it is alive, teeming with countless life forms. Each step you take is a connection, a dialogue with the earth. It is a reminder that you are a part of this intricate web of life, not separate from it.

As you walk, let your senses guide you. Observe the play of light and shadow, the myriad shades of green, and the intricate patterns of leaves and bark. Listen to the rustle of leaves, the chirping of birds, the whisper of the wind. Feel the coolness of the air, the warmth of the sun, the gentle caress of the breeze. Smell the earthy scent of the forest, the fragrance of flowers, the aroma of pine and cedar. Each sensation is a thread in the tapestry of the forest, weaving a story of life, growth, and interconnectedness.

Walking in the forest is not about reaching a destination. It is about being present, being aware, being connected. It is about moving in harmony with nature, matching your rhythm to the rhythm of the forest. It is about opening your heart to the beauty and wonder of the natural world and allowing it to nourish and rejuvenate your spirit.

So take that first step. Initiate the dance with nature. Let the forest guide you, teach you, heal you. And as you walk, remember that you are not alone. You are part of the forest, and the forest is part of you.

The Path of Awareness: Observing, Feeling, and Connecting

As you step into the lush embrace of the forest, you are not merely a visitor but a participant in a grand, timeless ballet. The Path of Awareness is not a physical trail marked by signs or worn by the passage of countless feet. It is an internal journey, a shift in perception that allows you to truly see, feel, and connect with the forest around you.

Begin by allowing your senses to awaken. The forest is a symphony of sensations, a tapestry woven from countless threads of sight, sound, scent, and touch. Look around you. Notice how the sunlight filters through the leaves, casting dappled shadows on the forest floor. Observe the myriad shades of green, the intricate patterns of bark, and the delicate dance of a leaf falling to the ground.

Listen. The forest speaks in whispers and sighs, in the rustle of leaves and the distant call of a bird. Each sound is a note in the forest's song, a melody that has been playing since the dawn of time. Close your eyes and let the music wash over you, seeping into your soul and resonating with your inner rhythm.

Inhale deeply. The scent of the forest is a heady mix of earth and greenery, of life in its most primal form. It is the aroma of growth, of decay, of the endless cycle of life and death that sustains the forest. Each breath you take is a communion, a sharing of life force between you and the forest.

Reach out and touch the world around you. Feel the rough texture of bark beneath your fingers, the cool dampness of moss, the fragile delicacy of a leaf. Each sensation is a word, a phrase in the language of the forest. As you walk, let your hands brush against the plants and trees around you, a silent greeting between old friends.

The Path of Awareness is a journey of connection, a dance of unity between you and the forest. As you walk, you are not merely observing the forest but becoming a part of it. You are the forest, and the forest is you. This realization, this deep, profound connection, is the essence of forest bathing. It is a balm for the soul, a salve for the spirit, a reminder of our place in the grand tapestry of life.

As you continue your journey, remember this feeling. Carry it with you, not just in the forest but all aspects of your life. The Path of Awareness does not end when you leave the forest. It is a journey that continues, step by step, with each breath you take.

The Symphony of Silence: Listening to the Unspoken

A symphony of silence exists in the forest's heart, where the air is pure, and the light filters through the canopy in mottled patterns. It is not the absence of sound but rather a harmonious blend of subtle whispers that the forest breathes into existence. This symphony is the unspoken language of the forest, which speaks not to our ears but to our souls.

As you walk mindfully, let your senses become attuned to this symphony. Let the rustle of leaves underfoot become the percussion, the sighing of the wind through the branches of the woodwinds, the distant call of a bird, the soloist. Each sound is a note in the forest's composition, a piece of the tranquil melody constantly written and rewritten with each passing moment.

Listening to this symphony requires a quiet mind and an open heart.

It requires you to step outside your thoughts, worries, and plans and be present in the moment. It requires you to listen with your ears and your entire being.

Feel the vibrations of the forest's song as they resonate within you. Notice how they ebb and flow with the rhythm of your breath and rise and fall with the beating of your heart. The forest speaks to you, sharing its wisdom, stories, and secrets.

In the silence, you may find answers to questions you didn't know you had. You may find peace amid turmoil and clarity amid confusion. You may find a sense of connection, a sense of belonging, a sense of home.

The symphony of silence is a gift from the forest, a reminder of the profound beauty and wisdom that exists in every moment if only we take the time to listen. As you continue your journey of mindful walking, carry this symphony with you. Let it guide your steps, nourish your soul, and remind you of the deep, unspoken connection between you and the natural world.

As we conclude this section, take a moment to reflect on your experience. What did you hear in the symphony of silence? What did the forest say to you? And most importantly, how will you carry this experience with you as you continue your forest bathing journey?

The Breath of Life: Synchronizing Your Breath with the Forest's Rhythm

In the heart of the forest, where the air is pure and the silence is profound, a rhythm pulses with life. It is a rhythm that is not heard but felt. It is the rhythm of the forest, the rhythm of life itself. Walking mindfully, you can synchronize your breath with this rhythm, creating a harmonious dance of life between you and the forest.

Breathing is the most fundamental of life's processes. It is the first thing we do when we are born and the last thing we do before we die. It is the constant companion of our existence, the silent witness to our joys and sorrows. And yet, we often take it for granted, forgetting its importance and potential for healing and rejuvenation.

In the forest, the act of breathing takes on a new dimension. The air is rich with the scent of pine and moss, the subtle perfume of wildflowers, and the earthy aroma of the soil. Each breath you take is a gift from the forest, a nourishing cocktail of oxygen and phytoncides, the natural chemicals released by trees that boost our immune system and reduce stress.

As you walk, focus on your breath. Feel the cool air entering your nostrils, filling your lungs, spreading life and energy throughout your body. Notice the slight pause, the moment of stillness, before you exhale, releasing the air back into the forest, a silent thank you for the gift you have received.

Try to match your breath with the rhythm of the forest. If you listen closely, you can hear it in the rustling of the leaves, the whispering of the wind, the distant call of a bird. It is a slow, steady rhythm, a peaceful lullaby that invites you to slow down, to let go of your worries and fears, to simply be.

Inhale deeply, drawing in the life-giving energy of the forest. Hold your breath for a moment, savoring the sensation of fullness, of being alive. Exhale slowly, releasing any tension or negativity, letting it flow out of you and dissolve into the forest.

With each breath, you become more attuned to the forest's rhythm, more connected to its life force. You are not just walking in the forest but becoming a part of it, a participant in the grand dance of life that unfolds in its depths.

As you continue your mindful walk, let your breath be your guide, your anchor in the present moment. Let it remind you of the simple joy of being alive and the beauty and wonder surrounding you. Let it fill you with gratitude for the forest and its many gifts, for the opportunity to walk in its embrace, breathe its air, and share in its rhythm.

In the forest, every breath is a celebration of life, a testament to the interconnectedness of all things. By synchronizing your breath with the forest's rhythm, you are not just forest bathing but engaging in a profound act of communion with nature, a sacred ritual of connection and renewal. In this dance of breath and rhythm, you will find peace, joy, and a sense of belonging that transcends words.

Reflecting on Your Journey and Looking Ahead to Future Forest Bathing Experiences

As we draw the curtain on this chapter, let us pause and reflect, like a tranquil pool mirroring the forest's verdant canopy. You have embarked on a journey of mindful walking, a dance with nature, where each step has been a gentle imprint on the forest floor, a silent conversation with the earth.

You have tuned into the forest's heartbeat, a rhythm that pulses beneath the bark of ancient trees and whispers through the rustling leaves. You have initiated a dance with nature that is as old as the wind and timeless as the sky. You have walked the path of awareness, observing, feeling, and connecting with the forest in a profound and deeply personal way.

You have listened to the symphony of silence, the unspoken language of the forest that speaks volumes in its quietude. You have synchronized your breath with the forest's rhythm, inhaling the crisp, clean air and exhaling any lingering stress or worry.

Now, as you stand at the edge of the forest, bathed in the soft, dappled light, take a moment to reflect on your journey. How do you feel? Has the forest changed you in any way? You may feel a sense of calm and tranquility, a renewed connection with nature, or a deeper understanding of yourself.

Looking ahead, imagine the countless forest bathing experiences that await you. Each visit to the forest will be a new adventure, a chance to deepen your connection with nature and continue your journey of mindful walking. The forest is a living, breathing entity, ever-changing with the seasons, and each visit will reveal new sights, sounds, and sensations to discover.

As you step out of the forest and back into the hustle and bustle of daily life, carry the forest with you. Let its tranquility seep into your everyday moments, its rhythm guide your steps, and its silence bring you peace. Remember, the forest is not just a place but a state of mind, a sanctuary where you can retreat whenever you need to recharge, rejuvenate, and reconnect with your true self.

So, until your next forest bathing experience, keep the forest in your heart, and let its wisdom guide you on your journey through life.

Chapter Summary

- Mindful walking is a journey of awareness and presence, where one immerses oneself in the tranquil embrace of nature, moving in harmony with the rhythm of the natural world.
- Tuning into the forest's heartbeat requires quieting the mind and opening the senses, feeling the rhythm of nature that speaks of the interconnectedness of all life.
- The first step into the forest initiates a dance with nature, where each step is a connection and dialogue with the earth, reminding us that we are part of this intricate web of life.
- The Path of Awareness is an internal journey that allows us to truly see, feel, and connect with the forest around us, becoming a part of it and realizing the deep, profound connection between us and nature.
- The Symphony of Silence in the forest is a harmonious blend of subtle whispers that speak not to our ears but to our souls, providing answers, peace, and a sense of connection.
- Synchronizing our breath with the forest's rhythm creates a harmonious dance of life between us and the forest, reminding us of the simple joy of being alive and the beauty surrounding us.
- Each visit to the forest is a new adventure, a chance to deepen our connection with nature and continue our journey of

mindful walking, revealing new sights, sounds, and sensations to discover.

- The forest is not just a place but a state of mind, a sanctuary where we can retreat whenever we need to recharge, rejuvenate, and reconnect with our true selves.

4

THE SYMPHONY OF THE FOREST: ENGAGING YOUR SENSES

In its tranquil grandeur, the forest extends an open invitation to all who seek solace, rejuvenation, and a deeper connection with the natural world. It is a realm where time seems to slow, where the frenetic pace of modern life is replaced by the gentle rhythm of the seasons, the ebb and flow of life in its most primal form.

As you step into this verdant cathedral, you are greeted by a symphony of sensations that engage each of your senses. The forest is not a silent, static entity but a living, breathing organism communicating in a language as old as the earth itself. It speaks in the rustle of leaves, the scent of damp earth, the soft touch of moss underfoot, the sight of dappled sunlight filtering through the canopy, and the taste of wild berries plucked straight from the bush.

This chapter is an invitation to immerse yourself in this symphony, to engage your senses in a way that perhaps you have not done since childhood. It is an invitation to experience the forest not as a mere backdrop to your outdoor activities but as a dynamic, sensory-rich environment that has the power to heal, inspire, and transform.

The forest is calling. Will you answer its call? Will you accept its invitation to step off the beaten path, wander beneath its towering trees, listen to its whispering leaves, breathe in its fragrant symphony, feel its textured canvas, and taste its hidden flavors?

If you do, you will discover that forest bathing is not merely a walk in the woods but a journey into the heart of nature itself. This journey engages all your senses and leaves you feeling refreshed, rejuvenated, and deeply connected to the world around you.

So, come. The forest is waiting. Its symphony is about to begin. And you, dear reader, are the honored guest.

The Visual Feast: Seeing the Forest in a New Light

In its grandeur and majesty, the forest is a visual banquet that invites us to partake in its splendor. As we enter its embrace, our eyes are greeted by a kaleidoscope of colors, shapes, and patterns dancing in the dappled sunlight. This is the forest's visual feast, a soothing and invigorating spectacle that invites us to see the world in a new light.

The forest is not merely a collection of trees but a living, breathing canvas of nature's artistry. Each tree, with its gnarled roots, sturdy trunk, and leafy canopy, is a masterpiece in its own right. The bark, with its intricate patterns of lines and cracks, is like an abstract painting, while the leaves, with their myriad shades of green, are like delicate brush strokes on a watercolor canvas.

As we delve deeper into the forest, our eyes are drawn to the play of light and shadow. The sun, filtering through the leafy canopy, casts a dappled pattern on the forest floor, creating a mesmerizing mosaic of light and dark. The shadows, shifting and changing with the sun's movement, add depth and dimension to the forest's landscape.

The forest is also a theater of movement. The rustling leaves, swaying branches, and scurrying creatures add a dynamic element to the forest's visual feast. Even the seemingly still trees are in constant motion, growing and changing with the seasons.

In the forest, we are invited to see not just with our eyes but with our hearts. Each element of the forest, from the towering trees to the tiny insects, is a testament to the beauty and complexity of nature. As we immerse ourselves in this visual feast, we are reminded of our connection to the natural world and our place within it.

The forest's visual feast is not just a spectacle to be observed but an experience to be savored. It invites us to slow down, look closely, and see the world with fresh eyes. It is a reminder that beauty is not just in the grand vistas but in the small details, the fleeting moments, and the subtle nuances. It is a call to see the world not just as it is but as it could be, filled with wonder, beauty, and possibility.

So, as you step into the forest, open your eyes wide. Let them feast on the forest's visual banquet. Let them be filled with the forest's colors, shapes, and patterns. Let them be captivated by the forest's play of light and shadow, its dance of movement and stillness. Let them see the forest and the world in a new light.

The Whispering Leaves: Listening to the Forest's Melody

In the heart of the forest, where the sunlight dapples through the lush canopy and the air is rich with the scent of earth and foliage, a symphony plays ceaselessly. It is a melody often overlooked, drowned out by the clamor of our thoughts and the noise of our busy lives. Yet, when we pause and allow ourselves to listen genuinely, we can hear the whispering leaves, the forest's own melody.

Close your eyes and lend your ears to the forest. At first, you might hear the apparent sounds: the rustling of leaves as a squirrel scampers up a tree, the distant call of a bird, and the soft sigh of the wind. But as you continue to listen and sink deeper into the tranquility of the forest, you will begin to discern the subtler notes of the forest's symphony.

The gentle pitter-patter of raindrops falling on the leaf-strewn floor, the soft rustle of a deer moving stealthily through the undergrowth, the faint hum of insects going about their day, the whispering leaves conversing with the wind. Each sound is a note, a chord, a phrase in the forest's melody.

Listening to the forest's symphony is about more than just hearing. It is about understanding, immersing yourself in the rhythm of nature, and allowing the forest's melody to resonate within you. It is about realizing that you are a part of this symphony, not a mere spectator.

The whispering leaves have much to say if only we take the time to listen. They speak of the changing seasons, the life that thrives in the forest, and the timeless wisdom of nature. They sing a song of peace, of harmony, of resilience.

As you listen to the whispering leaves and allow the forest's melody to wash over you, you will find a sense of calm enveloping you. Your thoughts will quieten, your heart will slow, your senses will awaken. You will feel rejuvenated, reconnected with the world around you, and reminded of nature's simple yet profound beauty.

So, the next time you find yourself in the heart of the forest, pause for a moment. Close your eyes, take a deep breath, and listen. Listen to the whispering leaves, to the forest's melody. Let it fill you, move you, and remind you of the beauty and tranquility in our world. For in the symphony of the forest, there is a song for each of us that speaks to our hearts and rejuvenates our souls.

The Fragrant Symphony: Smelling the Forest's Aromas

The forest is not just a visual spectacle but a fragrant symphony that plays a soothing melody to your senses. As you step deeper into the heart of the woods, allow your senses to be enveloped by the aromatic embrace of the forest.

Close your eyes and take a deep breath. The air is crisp, clean, and refreshing, a stark contrast to the artificial, recycled air of the urban jungle. The forest's perfume is a complex blend of scents, each note telling a different story, each aroma a character in the forest's narrative.

The earthy scent of the damp soil, rich and fertile, is the forest's foundation. It is the scent of life, growth, and the ceaseless cycle of birth, death, and rebirth. It is the smell of the forest floor, a complex tapestry woven from fallen leaves, decaying wood, and the countless organisms that call it home.

The sharp, resinous fragrance of pine needles pricks your senses, a poignant reminder of the evergreens that stand tall and unyielding, even in the harshest winters. It is a scent that speaks of resilience, endurance, and the forest's unwavering will to survive.

The sweet, floral aroma of blooming flowers wafts through the air, a delicate whisper of the forest's softer side. It is the scent of spring, renewal, and the forest's yearly rebirth in a riot of colors and fragrances.

And then there's the subtle, almost indiscernible scent of the forest's inhabitants. The musky smell of a deer that passed by, the tangy odor of a fox's den, the fresh scent of bird feathers. These scents remind you that the forest is not just a place but a living, breathing space teeming with life.

As you breathe in the forest's fragrant symphony, let it cleanse your lungs, mind, and soul. Let it ground you and connect you to the earth, nature, and the essence of life. And as you exhale, let go of your worries, stress, and fears. Let the forest's breeze carry them away, lost among the rustling leaves and towering trees.

The forest's fragrant symphony is a song of life, growth, and resilience. It is a song that speaks to the soul and resonates with the very core of our being. Once heard, it is a song that will forever echo in your heart, a lasting reminder of the forest's healing embrace.

The Textured Canvas: Feeling the Forest's Touch

The forest is a living, breathing entity, a textured canvas that invites you to explore its myriad sensations. It is a tactile symphony of textures ranging from the rough bark of ancient trees to the soft moss that carpets the forest floor.

As you step into the forest, your feet are greeted by the crunch of fallen leaves, the squish of damp earth, the solidity of rocks, and the springiness of moss. Each step is a new sensation, a new note in the forest's tactile symphony.

Reach out and touch the bark of a tree. Feel its roughness, its grooves and ridges, its knots and hollows. Each tree is written in the language of touch, a story of years weathered, storms survived, and seasons celebrated.

Run your fingers over the soft, velvety moss, a miniature forest within the forest. Each tiny frond is a world unto itself, a testament to the forest's ability to create and sustain life in the most unexpected places.

Feel the cool, smooth surface of a river stone, worn down by the relentless flow of water. It is a reminder of the forest's timeless rhythm, the ebb and flow of life that is its heartbeat.

Pick up a fallen leaf and trace its veins, a roadmap of life's journey from bud to maturity. It symbolizes the forest's cycle of life and death, a cycle that is as beautiful as it is relentless.

As you immerse yourself in the forest's tactile symphony, you begin to feel a deep connection with the natural world. You realize that you are not just a visitor in the forest but a part of it. You are a part of its symphony, a part of its story.

And as you leave the forest, you carry with you the memory of its touch, a lasting echo of the forest's symphony. It is a memory that will stay with you, a memory that will draw you back to the forest time and time again.

In the end, the forest's touch is not just a sensation but a connection, a bond that ties you to the natural world. It is a reminder of your place in the grand scheme of things and the beauty and wonder of the forest.

The Hidden Flavors: Tasting the Forest's Gifts

In the heart of the forest, where the sunlight dapples through the verdant canopy and the air is rich with the scent of earth and leaves, a hidden banquet of flavors is waiting to be discovered. This is not a feast for the eyes but for the palate, a subtle symphony of tastes that can only be experienced when one truly immerses oneself in the forest's embrace.

The forest is not merely a visual spectacle but a living, breathing entity that offers gifts to those willing to receive. The taste of the forest is as varied and complex as its ecosystem, a delicate balance of sweet, bitter, tangy, and earthy notes that dance on the tongue and awaken the senses.

Imagine the gentle kiss of morning dew on your lips, a taste as pure and refreshing as the forest air itself. The sweet nectar of a wildflower, sampled by a curious tongue, offers a burst of sunshine and summer in a single drop. The tart tang of a ripe berry, plucked from a bush heavy with fruit, reminds us of nature's generosity and the cycle of life and growth.

Even the air has a flavor, especially after a rain shower when the forest floor releases its earthy perfume. It's a taste as old as time, a primal memory that connects us to our ancestors who once roamed these woods and relied on these flavors for sustenance and survival.

The forest also offers more unexpected flavors. The slightly bitter taste of a leaf, the woody flavor of a twig chewed thoughtfully, the surprising sweetness of a sap droplet on the bark of a tree. These are not tastes we are accustomed to in our daily lives, but they are an integral part of the forest's rich tapestry of flavors.

As you wander through the forest, allow yourself to taste its gifts if it is safe to do so. Let your tongue become another exploration tool, another way to connect with the natural world. Each flavor is a note in the forest's symphony, a song that speaks of life, growth, and the eternal cycle of nature.

In tasting the forest's gifts, we not only engage our senses but also deepen our connection with the natural world. We become part of the forest, part of its symphony, and in doing so, we find a sense of peace and rejuvenation that can only be found in nature's embrace. The forest's flavors are a gift, a reminder of the simple, profound beauty of the natural world and the joy of being alive.

The Lasting Echo of the Forest's Symphony

As we draw the curtain on this immersive journey through the forest, we find ourselves standing at the edge of a profound realization. In its infinite wisdom and timeless beauty, the forest has offered us a symphony of experiences that have engaged our senses in ways we could have never imagined. However, the echoes of this symphony do not fade away as we step out of the forest's embrace. Instead, they linger, resonating within us and leaving a lasting imprint on our hearts and minds.

The forest's symphony is not merely a collection of isolated notes. It is a harmonious blend of sights, sounds, smells, textures, and tastes that have the power to transport us to a realm of tranquility and rejuvenation. The visual feast of verdant greens and dappled sunlight, the whispering leaves sharing ancient secrets, the fragrant symphony of earth and bloom, the textured canvas of bark and leaf, and the hidden flavors of nature's bounty - each of these elements has played a unique melody in our forest symphony.

As we leave the forest, we carry these melodies with us. They become a part of us, subtly influencing our thoughts, emotions, and actions. They remind us of the forest's invitation to slow down, breathe, and be present. They inspire us to seek beauty in the ordinary, listen to the whispers of nature, and savor life's simple pleasures.

The echoes of the forest's symphony gently remind us of our connection to the natural world. They remind us that we are not separate from nature but integral to it. They encourage us to respect and protect the natural world, cherish its beauty and diversity, and honor its wisdom and resilience.

In the hustle and bustle of our daily lives, these echoes can serve as a soothing balm, a source of comfort and inspiration. They can help us navigate life's challenges with grace and resilience, reminding us of nature's healing power, mindfulness's importance, and the joy of simple pleasures.

As we conclude this journey, let us take a moment to express our gratitude to the forest for its generous gifts. Let us commit to carrying the echoes of the forest's symphony in our hearts, allowing them to guide, inspire, and heal us. Let us remember that the forest is not just a place but a state of mind, a way of being, and a source of endless inspiration and wisdom. And let us look forward to our next forest bathing experience, knowing that the forest will always welcome us with open arms, ready to share its symphony again.

Chapter Summary

- The forest is a living, breathing entity that offers a symphony of sensory experiences, inviting us to engage our senses in a way that can be profoundly healing and rejuvenating.
- The visual feast of the forest is a kaleidoscope of colors, shapes, and patterns that invites us to see the world in a new light, reminding us of the beauty and complexity of nature.
- The forest's symphony is not just audible but also a language of understanding, immersing oneself in the rhythm of nature, allowing the forest's melody to resonate within us, and realizing that we are a part of this symphony.
- The forest's fragrant symphony is a complex blend of scents that tells a different story, each aroma a character in the forest's narrative, reminding us of our connection to the natural world.
- The forest is a textured canvas that invites us to explore its myriad sensations, reminding us that we are not just visitors in the forest but a part of it, a part of its symphony, a part of its story.
- The forest offers a hidden banquet of flavors waiting to be discovered, each flavor a note in the forest's symphony, a song that speaks of life, growth, and the eternal cycle of nature.
- The echoes of the forest's symphony linger, resonating within us, leaving a lasting imprint on our hearts and minds and subtly influencing our thoughts, emotions, and actions.
- The forest's symphony serves as a gentle reminder of our connection to the natural world, encouraging us to respect and protect the natural world, cherish its beauty and diversity, and honor its wisdom and resilience.

5

THE FOREST'S HEALING TOUCH: PHYSICAL AND MENTAL HEALTH BENEFITS

We find a sanctuary in the serenity of the forest, where the air is rich with the scent of damp earth and the rustling leaves whisper ancient secrets. A sanctuary not built by human hands but by the patient, tireless work of nature herself. This is a place where we can shed the weight of our worries, where the clamor of the modern world fades into insignificance, replaced by the soothing symphony of the forest. This is the realm of forest bathing, a practice that invites us to immerse ourselves in the healing embrace of the woods.

Forest bathing, or Shinrin-yoku, is not about vigorous hiking or strenuous physical activity. It is about stillness, about allowing the forest to envelop us, to seep into our senses and touch our souls. It is about opening our hearts to the forest's healing touch, about letting the forest breathe life into us, rejuvenating our bodies and minds.

The forest is a living, breathing entity, a complex network of life that has evolved over millions of years. It is a world teeming with life, from the towering trees reaching for the sky to the tiny organisms that make their home in the rich, fertile soil. Each element of the forest, each leaf, each bird's song, and each ray of sunlight filtering through the canopy contributes to a healing environment that is as old as life itself.

As we step into the forest, we are stepping into a world that operates on a different rhythm, a rhythm that is in tune with the natural cycles of life. The forest's rhythm is slow, patient, and enduring. It is a rhythm that our bodies recognize that resonates with the deepest parts of our being. It is a rhythm that heals.

In this chapter, we will explore the healing power of the forest, delving into the physical and mental health benefits of forest bathing. We will learn about the forest's symphony and how the sounds of nature influence our well-being. We will discover the green prescription and understand the physical health benefits of forest bathing. We will find sanctuary for our minds, learning about the mental health advantages of immersion in nature. We will delve into the forest's aromatherapy, understanding the healing power of phytoncides. We will hear personal stories and experiences of the healing impact of forest bathing.

As we journey through this chapter, let us open our hearts and minds to the forest's healing touch, rekindling our ancient bond with the forest for holistic health. Let us embrace the forest's healing embrace, immersing ourselves in nature's tranquil, rejuvenating power.

The Forest's Symphony: How Nature Sounds Influence Our Well-being

In the heart of the forest, a symphony is perpetually in session. It is a concert that requires no tickets, no grand halls, and no formal attire. It is a performance that is as old as the earth itself, yet each rendition is unique, fresh, and invigorating. This is the forest's symphony, a harmonious blend of sounds that has the power to heal, rejuvenate, and inspire.

The forest's symphony is not merely an auditory experience; it is a sensory journey that begins with the gentle rustling of leaves, the distant call of a bird, the soft murmur of a brook, and the whispering wind. These sounds, subtle and soothing, have a profound influence on our well-being. They act as a balm to our overstimulated minds, offering a respite from the cacophony of our urban existence.

Scientific studies have shown that exposure to natural sounds can lower blood pressure, reduce stress hormones, and improve mood. The rhythmic patterns of nature, such as the repetitive sound of water dripping or leaves rustling, can induce relaxation akin to meditation. This is because these sounds often fall within the range of frequencies known to induce calm and relaxation in the human brain.

The forest's symphony also plays a crucial role in restoring our cognitive functions. The constant barrage of noise in urban environments can lead to cognitive fatigue, impairing our ability to focus and process information. On the other hand, the tranquil sounds of the forest can enhance our attention span and creativity. They provide a soothing backdrop that allows our minds to unwind, reset, and rejuvenate.

Listening to the forest's symphony is not a passive act. It is an immersive experience that invites us to engage with our surroundings and attune our senses to the subtle shifts in the forest's soundscape. It is an opportunity to practice mindfulness, to be present in the moment, and to connect with nature on a deeper level.

The forest's symphony is a testament to the healing power of nature. It is a gentle reminder of our intrinsic connection to the natural world, a connection that can nourish our physical and mental health. So, the next time you find yourself in the embrace of the forest, close your eyes, take a deep breath, and listen. Let the forest's symphony wash over you, heal you; let it play the melody of well-being in your heart.

The Green Prescription: Physical Health Benefits of Forest Bathing

In the heart of the forest, where the sunlight filters through the verdant canopy, casting dappled shadows on the forest floor, lies a potent remedy for our physical ailments. This remedy, as ancient as the forest itself, is the practice of forest bathing. The Japanese call it Shinrin-yoku, but regardless of the name, the essence remains the same - immersing oneself in the forest environment to reap its healing benefits.

The forest, in its tranquil grandeur, is a natural pharmacy. Its green prescription, written in the language of rustling leaves and whispering winds, offers many physical health benefits. Forest bathing is not merely a walk in the woods but a deliberate and mindful immersion in nature, a gentle communion with the forest that engages all our senses.

We inhale a cocktail of beneficial substances as we breathe in the forest air. Among these are phytoncides which, as we discovered in earlier chapters, are volatile organic compounds released by trees and plants. These substances, while serving as a plant's defense mechanism against insects and bacteria, profoundly impact our health. Research has shown that exposure to phytoncides boosts our immune system function by increasing the activity of natural killer cells, our body's defense against viruses and cancer.

The forest's green prescription also includes a dose of cardiovascular health. The calming effect of the forest environment reduces stress, a significant risk factor for heart disease. The serene forest setting lowers blood pressure, heart rate, and levels of the stress hormone cortisol. The result is a healthier heart, more attuned to the natural rhythms of life.

Moreover, forest bathing aids in combating obesity and diabetes. The physical activity involved, though gentle, helps in maintaining a healthy weight and improving insulin sensitivity. The forest's soothing ambiance encourages us to slow down and move at nature's unhurried pace, promoting a more active lifestyle.

The forest's healing touch extends to our respiratory system as well. The clean, fresh air of the forest, rich in oxygen and free from urban pollutants, relieves those suffering from respiratory ailments. Breathing in this air is like giving our lungs a refreshing cleanse, enhancing our overall respiratory health.

The green prescription of forest bathing is a testament to the healing power of nature. It is a call to return to our roots, to seek solace and rejuvenation in the embrace of the forest. As we immerse ourselves in this verdant sanctuary, we allow the forest to heal us, restore our physical health, and rekindle our ancient bond with nature.

The Mind's Sanctuary: Mental Health Advantages of Immersion in Nature

The forest is not a sanctuary built of stone and mortar, but it is alive, breathing, and ever-changing. It is a sanctuary for the mind, a haven where the tumultuous waves of thoughts and emotions find their calm.

The forest, with its serene beauty and tranquil silence, profoundly impacts our mental health. It is not just a place for physical exercise but a space for mental rejuvenation. The forest's gentle whispers, the rustling of leaves, and the soft murmur of a distant stream all work in harmony to soothe our minds, ease our worries, and transport us to peaceful contemplation.

When we immerse ourselves in this natural sanctuary, we are not merely observers but participants in a grand, interconnected dance of life. We become part of the forest, and the forest becomes part of us. This deep connection, this sense of belonging, can have a profound impact on our mental well-being. It can alleviate feelings of loneliness and isolation and foster a sense of inner peace and contentment.

Moreover, the forest, with its ever-changing seasons, serves as a gentle reminder of the impermanence of life. The vibrant green leaves of spring give way to the fiery hues of autumn, only to be replaced by the stark beauty of winter. This birth, growth, decay, and rebirth cycle can help us understand our life's transitions and changes. It can help us accept and embrace the ebb and flow of life rather than resist it.

The forest also teaches us the art of mindfulness. As we walk along its winding paths, listen to the symphony of nature, and breathe in the fresh, earthy scent of the forest, we become more present, more aware of our surroundings, and more in tune with our inner selves. This heightened awareness can help us manage stress, reduce anxiety, and enhance our mental health.

In the forest, we find a sanctuary for our minds, where we can heal, grow, and rejuvenate. It is a place where we can reconnect with ourselves, nature, and the rhythm of life. So, let us step into the forest, let us immerse ourselves in its healing embrace, and let us discover the profound mental health benefits that it has to offer.

The Forest's Aromatherapy: Understanding the Healing Power of Phytoncides

The green pharmacy of the forest is not housed within walls, nor does it have a counter where prescriptions are filled. Instead, its medicine is diffused in the air, a subtle, aromatic blend of organic compounds known as phytoncides.

Phytoncides, derived from the Greek words 'phyton' meaning 'plant' and 'cide' meaning 'kill,' are volatile organic compounds emitted by plants and trees. They serve as a natural defense mechanism against harmful insects and microorganisms. But these forest-born essences offer more than just protection for the trees; they are a balm for the human spirit and body.

You are also inhaling these phytoncides as you breathe in the forest air, rich with the scent of pine needles, damp earth, and the subtle perfume of wildflowers. They enter your body, whispering to your cells in a language as old as life itself. This is the forest's aromatherapy, a gentle yet powerful healer.

Scientific studies have shown that exposure to phytoncides can have significant health benefits. They can boost the immune system, increasing the activity of natural killer cells that help to fight disease. They can lower blood pressure, reduce stress hormones, and improve concentration and mental clarity.

Imagine, if you will, a walk in the forest as a therapeutic journey. With each step, you are moving deeper into a realm of healing. You draw in the forest's essence with each breath, allowing it to mingle with your own. The trees stand as silent therapists, their phytoncides a gift of health and well-being.

The forest's aromatherapy is a testament to the interconnectedness of all life. It reminds us that we are not separate from nature but a part of it. As we breathe in the forest's healing compounds, we participate in a cycle of mutual benefit, a dance of give and take that has been ongoing for millions of years.

In the end, understanding the healing power of phytoncides is about more than just recognizing the physical benefits they offer. It is about acknowledging our deep, intrinsic connection with the natural world. It is about embracing the forest's healing touch and, in doing so, finding a path to our own well-being.

Personal Stories of Forest Bathing's Healing Impact

Many have found solace, strength, and healing through the forest's embrace. This chapter is dedicated to their stories, to the transformative power of the forest that has touched their lives in profound ways.

Case Study 1

Our first tale is of a woman named Clara. A high-powered executive, Clara was a stranger to the concept of rest. Her life was a whirlwind of meetings, deadlines, and stress. One day, her body rebelled against the relentless pace, and she found herself bedridden, diagnosed with chronic fatigue syndrome. It was during her recovery that she discovered forest bathing. She began with short, gentle walks in the nearby woodland. The forest, she said, was like a balm to her frayed nerves. The rustle of leaves, the chirping of birds, the cool, clean air - it was as if each element of the forest was whispering to her, urging her to slow down, breathe, and heal. Over time, Clara regained her strength, and more importantly, she learned the value of balance and rest.

Case Study 2

Next, we have the story of Tom, a war veteran grappling with post-traumatic stress disorder. The memories of war were a constant shadow, a specter that haunted his days and nights. It was in the forest that Tom found a semblance of peace. He described the forest as a sanctuary where he could escape the ghosts of his past. The towering trees stood as silent sentinels, their steadfast presence a comforting reminder of the enduring power of life. With its gentle rhythms and soothing sounds, the forest became a place of refuge and healing for Tom.

Case Study 3

Lastly, we meet Lily, a young woman battling depression. She felt disconnected from the world in the depths of her despair, lost in a sea of sadness. It was her therapist who suggested forest bathing. Hesitant at first, Lily soon found herself drawn to the forest's tranquil beauty. She spoke of how the forest seemed to absorb her sorrow, replacing it with a sense of calm and serenity. The simple act of observing the forest, of being present and in the moment, helped Lily reconnect with herself and the world around her.

These stories, and countless others, are a testament to the healing power of the forest. They remind us that we are a part of nature, not apart from it. They urge us to seek solace in the forest's embrace, listen to its symphony, and breathe in its healing aromas. For in the heart of the forest, we can find our own hearts, healed and whole.

Rekindling Our Ancient Bond with the Forest for Holistic Health

As the sun dips below the horizon, painting the sky with hues of orange and purple, we find ourselves at the end of our journey, standing at the edge of the forest, our hearts filled with a newfound understanding and appreciation for its healing touch. We have explored the forest's symphony, green prescription, sanctuary for the mind, and unique aromatherapy. We have heard the personal stories of those who have found solace and healing in its embrace. Now, it is time to reflect on wha we have learned and how we can rekindle our ancient bond with the forest for holistic health.

Our ancestors lived in harmony with nature, their lives intertwined with the rhythms of the earth and the forest. They understood the healing power of the forest, the way it could soothe a troubled mind, heal a weary body, and rejuvenate a tired spirit. This ancient wisdom, this deep connection with the forest, is something that many of us have lost in our modern, fast-paced lives. But it is not something that is lost forever. It is a bond that can be rekindled, a relationship that can be renewed.

Rekindling our bond with the forest begins with a simple step: stepping into the forest. It is about immersing ourselves in its beauty, tranquility, and healing energy. It is about letting the forest's symphony wash over us, letting its green prescription heal us, letting its sanctuary calm our minds, and letting its aromatherapy cleanse our spirits. It is about letting the forest touch, heal, and transform us.

But it is not just about taking from the forest. It is also about giving back, respecting and preserving the forest, and ensuring that future generations can feel its healing touch. It is about understanding that our health and the health of the forest are intertwined and that we are also healing ourselves by healing the forest.

As we leave the forest, we carry its healing touch with us. We carry its symphony in our hearts, its green prescription in our bodies, its sanctuary in our minds, and its aromatherapy in our spirits. We carry the stories of those who have found healing in its embrace, and we carry the hope of rekindling our ancient bond with the forest for holistic health.

The forest is not just a place. It is a healer, a sanctuary, a symphony, an aromatherapist. It is a part of us, and we are a part of it. By embracing the forest's healing touch and rekindling our ancient bond, we can find a path to holistic health that leads us back to our true selves, roots, and forests.

Chapter Summary

- Forest bathing, or Shinrin-yoku, immerses oneself in the forest environment, allowing the forest to envelop us and rejuvenate our bodies and minds. It operates on a rhythm that resonates with our being and promotes healing.
- The forest's symphony, a harmonious blend of nature sounds, profoundly influences our well-being. These sounds can induce a state of relaxation, restore cognitive functions, and enhance our attention span and creativity.
- The forest offers a green prescription for physical health. The calming effect of the forest environment also promotes cardiovascular health and aids in combating obesity and diabetes.
- Phytoncides, volatile organic compounds emitted by plants and trees, are a natural defense mechanism against harmful insects and microorganisms. Exposure to phytoncides can have significant health benefits, including boosting the immune system, lowering blood pressure, reducing stress hormones, and improving concentration and mental clarity.
- The forest serves as a sanctuary for our minds, helping to alleviate loneliness and isolation and fostering a sense of inner peace and contentment. It also teaches us the art of mindfulness, helping us manage stress, reduce anxiety, and enhance our overall mental health.
- Rekindling our ancient bond with the forest for holistic health involves immersing ourselves in its beauty, tranquility, and healing energy. It also involves giving back to the forest, respecting and preserving it for future generations.
- The forest is not just a place but a healer, a sanctuary, a symphony, and an aromatherapist. By embracing the forest's healing touch and rekindling our ancient bond with it, we can find a path to holistic health.

6

THE LANGUAGE OF TREES: UNDERSTANDING FOREST ECOLOGY

As the first light of dawn gently pierces the veil of night, the forest awakens. The symphony of the forest begins with a soft prelude, a rustling whisper of leaves stirred by the morning breeze. It is an ancient and ever-new, timeless melody that speaks of life's enduring rhythm. This is the opening act of our journey into the heart of the forest, which will immerse us in the profound wisdom and healing power of trees.

The forest is not merely a collection of trees standing in silent isolation. It is a vibrant, interconnected community, a living, breathing entity that pulsates with life. Each tree, from the towering oak to the humble birch, plays a unique role in this grand orchestra. They are the musicians who create the symphony of the forest, which resonates with the deepest chords of our being.

As we delve deeper into the forest, we begin to perceive the subtle harmonies that underpin this symphony. The rustle of leaves is not just a random sound but a language, a form of communication that trees use to share vital information. The roots beneath our feet are not just anchors but intricate networks that connect trees in a web of mutual support and exchange. The air we breathe is not just a life-giving necessity but a testament to trees' crucial role in regulating our planet's climate.

The forest is a place of healing and rejuvenation. The simple act of walking among trees, of bathing in their presence, can have profound effects on our physical and mental well-being. This is the power of forest bathing, a power that is rooted in the very essence of trees.

As we journey through this chapter, we will explore the fascinating world of forest ecology. We will learn about the language of trees, the green network that binds them together, and their vital role in our world. We will discover the therapeutic power of trees and the importance of biodiversity in maintaining the health and vitality of our forests.

In the end, we will understand that the wisdom of the woods is not a distant, elusive concept but a tangible reality that we can embrace and incorporate into our lives. The symphony of the forest is not just a melody that we listen to but a song that we are a part of, a song that invites us to join in its harmonious dance.

So, let us begin our journey. Let us step into the forest, breathe in its healing air, listen to its symphony, and immerse ourselves in its tranquil, rejuvenating embrace. For in the heart of the forest, we will find not just trees but a reflection of our inner nature, a mirror that reveals our deep connection to the earth and all life.

The Rooted Conversations: How Trees Communicate

In the calm tranquility of the forest, a conversation is taking place. It is not one that we can hear with our ears, but rather, it is a dialogue that unfolds beneath our feet in the intricate network of roots and fungal threads that weave through the soil. This is the language of trees, a silent symphony of signals and messages that form the backbone of the forest's communication system.

Contrary to what we might initially believe, trees are not solitary beings. They are deeply interconnected, their lives intertwined in complex relationships across species and generations. Beneath the leafy canopy, in the stillness of the forest floor, trees engage in a ceaseless exchange of information, nutrients, and water, a process scientists have aptly named the "Wood-Wide Web."

This communication system is facilitated by mycorrhizal fungi, microscopic organisms that form symbiotic relationships with tree roots. The fungi extend their thread-like hyphae into the soil, creating a vast underground network connecting individual trees to one another. Trees can send and receive signals through this network, alerting each other to threats, sharing resources, and even nurturing their young.

Imagine a tree that harmful insects have invaded. Through the Wood-Wide Web, it can send out distress signals, alerting its neighbors to the danger. In response, the surrounding trees can ramp up their production of defensive chemicals, effectively inoculating themselves against the impending threat.

Similarly, when a tree is dying, it can redistribute its nutrients through the network, ensuring its legacy lives on in the forest it leaves behind. This is not a one-way street, however. Trees also receive nutrients and water from their neighbors in times of need.

In this light, the forest emerges not as a collection of individual trees but as a single, living organism, a community bound together by the language of roots and fungi. It is a testament to the power of connection, mutual aid, and cooperation, principles that are as vital to the health of a forest as they are to our own well-being.

As we immerse ourselves in the soothing embrace of the forest, let us remember this silent conversation that unfolds beneath our feet. Let us listen, not with our ears, but with our hearts, to the trees' wisdom and the lessons they teach us about interdependence, resilience, and the healing power of community. In the language of trees, we find a mirror to our humanity, a reminder of our deep-rooted connection to the natural world.

The Green Network: Exploring the Wood-Wide Web

n the heart of the forest, beneath the flourishing canopy and the dappled sunlight, lies a hidden world that hums with life. It is a world unseen, a world unheard, but a world that is as vital to the forest as the air we breathe. This is the world of the Wood-Wide Web, a complex network of roots and fungi that connects trees in a symbiotic relationship of shared resources and communication.

Imagine, if you will, the forest floor as a bustling city with its own highways and byways and traffic of nutrients and information. Standing tall and serene, the trees are not solitary entities but part of a vast, interconnected community. Their roots, intertwined with delicate threads of fungi, form an underground web that spans the entire forest.

This network, known as the mycorrhizal network, is the lifeline of the forest. It allows trees to share water, nutrients, and even information with each other. A tree suffering from drought can send a distress signal through the network, prompting its neighbors to share their water. A tree under attack from pests can warn its fellows, triggering a forest-wide defense mechanism. It is a system of mutual aid and cooperation, a testament to the interconnectedness of all life.

The Wood-Wide Web is not just a means of survival but also a means of nurturing. Older, more established trees, known as 'mother trees,' use the network to support their offspring, funneling nutrients to the saplings and helping them grow. It is a form of parental care that is as tender as it is essential, a gentle whisper of life in the quiet of the forest.

Exploring the Wood-Wide Web is like delving into the heart of the forest and the essence of its being. It is a journey of discovery, of understanding, of connection. It is a reminder that we, too, are part of a larger whole and are rooted in the earth and entwined with all life.

As we immerse ourselves in the tranquility of the forest, breathe in its healing air, and bathe in its soothing green light, let us remember the Wood-Wide Web. Let us remember the language of the trees, the forest symphony, and the woods' wisdom. Let us remember, and let us learn For in understanding the forest, we understand ourselves. And in under standing ourselves, we find peace.

The Forest's Breath: The Role of Trees in Climate Regulation

A silent exchange occurs in the heart of the forest, where the sunlight filters through the leafy canopy. This is the forest's breath, a ceaseless cycle of inhalation and exhalation that is as vital to our planet's health as our respiration is to us.

Trees, in their serene and steadfast way, are the lungs of the Earth. They inhale carbon dioxide, a greenhouse gas contributing to global warming, and exhale oxygen, the life-giving element that sustains most organisms. This process, known as photosynthesis, is a quiet yet powerful act of transformation that underpins the health of our global ecosystem.

Imagine, if you will, the forest at dawn. As the first rays of sunlight pierce the canopy, they touch upon the leaves, setting in motion a process as old as life itself. In their emerald splendor, the leaves absorb the sunlight, using their energy to convert the inhaled carbon dioxide and water into glucose, a sugar fueling the tree's growth and development. Oxygen, a by-product of this process, is released back into the atmosphere, a gift of life from the forest to the world.

But the forest's breath does more than regulate the composition of our atmosphere. It also plays a crucial role in climate regulation. By absorbing carbon dioxide, trees help to mitigate the impact of human-induced climate change. They act as carbon sinks, storing the absorbed carbon in their trunks, branches, leaves, roots, and the soil they stand in.

Furthermore, forests influence local and regional climates by regulating water cycles. Through a process known as transpiration, trees release water vapor into the atmosphere, contributing to cloud formation and precipitation. This nourishes the forest itself and impacts weather patterns and water availability in surrounding areas.

As we immerse ourselves in the tranquil embrace of the forest, let us remember the silent work being done by these towering sentinels of the Earth. Each breath we take is a testament to their ceaseless labor, a reminder of our deep and enduring connection with the natural world.

In understanding the language of trees, we come to appreciate their vital role in our world and our responsibility to protect and preserve them. For in their quiet, steadfast way, they are the guardians of our climate, the breath of our planet, the silent heartbeat of the Earth.

The Healing Canopy: The Therapeutic Power of Trees

In the heart of the forest, beneath the canopy, a realm of tranquility and healing exists. This is a world where the air is rich with the scent of damp earth and the whispers of leaves, where the sunlight filters through the foliage, casting dappled patterns on the forest floor. Here, in this serene sanctuary, we find the therapeutic power of trees.

Trees, in their silent, steadfast way, have been the guardians of our planet for millions of years. They have witnessed the passage of time, the changing of seasons, and the ebb and flow of life. Their roots delve deep into the earth, drawing nourishment and strength, while their branches reach towards the sky, embracing the light. They stand as symbols of resilience and growth, offering lessons of patience and perseverance.

But beyond their symbolic significance, trees hold a more tangible, physiological power to heal. Forest bathing is based on this very principle. It suggests that spending time under the canopy of a living forest can lead to significant health benefits through the presence of phytoncides in the forest air.

Moreover, the forest environment, with its soothing sounds of rustling leaves, chirping birds, and trickling streams, can have a calming effect on our minds. It can reduce stress, anxiety, and depression, promoting peace and well-being. In its quiet, unassuming way, the forest invites us to slow down, breathe, and reconnect with our inner selves and the world around us.

The healing power of trees extends to their ability to absorb carbon dioxide and release oxygen, purifying the air we breathe. They also act as natural filters, removing harmful pollutants and providing cleaner, healthier air. By doing so, they contribute to our physical health and play a crucial role in the health of our planet.

In the grand tapestry of life, trees are not merely passive observers. They are active participants, nurturing life, fostering growth, and offering healing. They speak a language of resilience and renewal, of connection and care. As we walk beneath their healing canopy, we are reminded of our place in the natural world, of the delicate balance, and of the profound wisdom held in the forest's heart.

So, let us listen to the trees' whispers, learn their language, and embrace the healing power they offer. In doing so, we not only nurture our own health and well-being but also contribute to the health and sustainability of our planet.

The Forest's Guardians: The Importance of Biodiversity

The forest is home to towering trees and the myriad creatures that call the forest their home. They are the guardians of the forest, each playing a vital role in maintaining the delicate balance of this complex ecosystem. This section delves into the importance of biodiversity, the forest's guardians, in the grand symphony of the woods.

Biodiversity, in its simplest form, refers to the variety of life in a particular habitat or ecosystem. In a forest, it encompasses everything from the smallest microorganism in the soil to the largest mammal that roams its depths. Each species, no matter how seemingly insignificant, contributes to the overall health and resilience of the forest.

Consider the humble earthworm, often overlooked and underappreciated. These tiny creatures are the unsung heroes of the forest floor, tirelessly working to break down organic matter and enrich the soil. This process nourishes the trees and supports the growth of other plants, creating a lush understory that provides food and shelter for a host of animals.

Similarly, the larger forest inhabitants, such as deer and birds, play their part in the life cycle. They help in the dispersal of seeds, ensuring the propagation of trees and other plant species. Predators, in turn, keep the population of these herbivores in check, preventing overgrazing and maintaining the diversity of plant life.

The forest's guardians also include the trees themselves. Different tree species offer different resources, from food to shelter, attracting wildlife and supporting a rich tapestry of life. The biodiversity of trees also enhances the forest's resilience, enabling it to withstand diseases and pests that could decimate a monoculture.

In essence, biodiversity is the lifeblood of the forest. It is a testament to the interconnectedness of all living things, a delicate dance of give-and-take that has been perfected over millennia. It is a reminder that every creature, plant, and microorganism has a role in the grand scheme of things.

As we immerse ourselves in the tranquility of the forest, let us not forget the silent guardians surrounding us. Let us appreciate the biodiversity that breathes life into the forest, makes each visit a unique experience, and teaches us the value of balance and harmony. By understanding and respecting these guardians, we enrich our forest bathing experience and contribute to preserving these magnificent ecosystems for generations to come.

Embracing the Wisdom of the Woods

As we draw the curtain on this verdant journey, we find ourselves standing at the edge of the forest, our senses heightened, our minds enriched, and our hearts filled with a newfound respect for the wisdom of the woods. In its tranquil silence, the forest has spoken volumes, teaching us lessons that resonate deep within our souls.

The forest is not merely a collection of trees, plants, and wildlife. It is a living, breathing entity, a complex network of life that thrives on cooperation and mutual support. The trees' roots entwined in a silent conversation have shown us the power of connection and community. They whisper to each other through the wood-wide web, sharing resources, sending warnings, and nurturing their young. This interconnectedness, this unity in diversity, is a lesson we can carry into our lives, reminding us of the strength in unity and the beauty that blooms in diversity.

The forest's breath, the gentle rustle of leaves in the wind, and the soft sigh of oxygen released into the atmosphere have taught us about trees vital role in climate regulation. They are the lungs of our planet, inhaling carbon dioxide and exhaling life-giving oxygen, a silent yet powerful testament to the importance of balance in nature and our lives.

The healing canopy of the forest, with its therapeutic power, has shown us the path to rejuvenation and well-being. Forest bathing, the simple act of immersing oneself in the forest atmosphere, can heal our bodies, calm our minds, and soothe our spirits. It is a gentle reminder of the healing power of nature and the importance of reconnecting with our roots.

The forest's guardians, the myriad species that call it home, have shown us the importance of biodiversity. Each creature, no matter how small, plays a crucial role in maintaining the balance of the ecosystem. Their presence reminds us of our responsibility to protect and preserve the natural world, for in its survival lies our own.

As we step out of the forest, we carry its wisdom, lessons, and tranquility with us. We leave behind the noise and chaos of our everyday lives and enter a world of serenity and harmony. We have learned to listen to the trees' language, understand their silent conversations, appreciate their role in our world, and embrace their wisdom.

In its timeless wisdom, the forest has shown us the way to a more mindful, balanced, and fulfilling life. It has taught us to value connection, cherish diversity, respect the balance of nature, and embrace the healing power of the natural world. As we move forward, let us carry these lessons in our hearts, live in harmony with nature, and embrace the wisdom of the woods.

Chapter Summary

- The forest is a vibrant, interconnected community of trees, each playing a unique role in the ecosystem. The rustle of leaves is a form of communication, and the roots form intricate networks that connect trees in a web of mutual support and exchange.

- Trees communicate through a complex network of roots and fungal threads called the "Wood-Wide Web." This silent symphony of signals and messages allows trees to share vital information, nutrients, and water.
- The Wood-Wide Web is a lifeline of the forest, allowing trees to share resources and information. It also enables older, established trees to support their offspring, demonstrating a form of parental care.
- Trees play a crucial role in climate regulation. Through photosynthesis, they absorb carbon dioxide and release oxygen, acting as the lungs of the Earth. They also influence local and regional climates by regulating water cycles.
- Spending time in the forest, or forest bathing, can have significant health benefits. The forest air is filled with phytoncides, which boost immune system function, reduce blood pressure, and improve mood and sleep patterns.
- Biodiversity is vital to the health and resilience of the forest. Every creature, plant, and microorganism plays a role in the ecosystem, contributing to the overall balance and harmony of the forest.
- The forest teaches us valuable lessons about interdependence, resilience, and the healing power of community. It reminds us of our deep-rooted connection to the natural world and our responsibility to protect and preserve it.
- The forest offers a path to rejuvenation and well-being, teaching us to value connection, cherish diversity, respect the balance of nature, and embrace the healing power of the natural world. It shows us the way to a more mindful, balanced, and fulfilling life.

7

FOREST BATHING THROUGH THE SEASONS: A YEAR-ROUND GUIDE

In the heart of the forest, time dances to a different rhythm. In its infinite wisdom, the forest does not adhere to the ticking of clocks or the turning of calendar pages. Instead, it follows a more ancient, more profound cadence - the symphony of the seasons. Each season's unique melody brings a new chapter in the forest's ongoing saga, a fresh perspective to our forest bathing journey.

Forest bathing is an immersive, sensory experience that invites us to connect with the forest's soul, to bathe in its essence. As we step into the forest, we step into a world that is alive, breathing, and ever-changing. We become part of the forest's narrative, woven into its tapestry of life.

The forest's seasonal symphony is a celebration of change, a testament to the forest's resilience and adaptability. Each season brings its own unique charm, its own distinct energy. Winter's hush, spring's awakening, summer's embrace, and autumn's farewell play a vital role in the forest's lifecycle, each offering a unique backdrop for our forest bathing experience.

With its silent serenity, winter invites us into a world of stillness, where every snow-cloaked tree stands as a sentinel of tranquility. With its rebirth of life, spring paints the forest in green hues as life stirs amidst the verdant canopies. With its warm whisper, summer bathes the forest in golden light as sun-dappled leaves sway in the gentle breeze. With its rustling lullaby, autumn bids farewell with a cascade of falling foliage, a spectacle of colors that warms the heart as the air grows crisp.

As we journey through the seasons, we learn to adapt, to flow with the forest's ebb and flow. We learn to embrace the changing seasons, find beauty in each moment, and see the forest not just as a static entity but as a dynamic, living organism that grows, changes, and evolves.

This chapter will explore the forest's seasonal symphony, guiding you through a year-round forest bathing experience. We will delve into the unique charm of each season, offering insights and tips on adapting your forest bathing practice to the changing seasons.

So, let us embark on this journey together, immersing ourselves in the forest's seasonal symphony, bathing in its tranquil, rejuvenating energy. Let us embrace the forest's endless cycle of renewal and reflection, finding peace, solace, and connection in its ever-changing beauty.

Winter's Hush: The Silent Serenity of Snow-Cloaked Trees

As the last leaves of autumn fall, the forest transitions into a season of profound tranquility. With its hushed whispers and serene landscapes, winter offers a unique experience for the forest bather. This season invites you to immerse yourself in the quiet beauty of the winter forest, a world transformed by a blanket of snow and the crisp, clean air.

The forest in winter is a realm of stillness, where a profound silence replaces the usual rustling and chirping. This silence is not empty but instead filled with peace and calm that can only be found in the heart of winter. Now devoid of their leafy attire, the trees stand as stoic sentinels, their bare branches reaching out to the sky in silent prayer. Each one is adorned with a delicate layer of snow, transforming the forest into a monochrome masterpiece.

As you step into this winter wonderland, the crunch of your footsteps on the fresh snow is the only sound that dares to break the silence. The crisp and refreshing air fills your lungs with a cool freshness that revitalizes your senses. Each breath you take reminds you of the forest's enduring life force, even amid winter's slumber.

Standing tall and serene, the snow-cloaked trees invite you to pause and reflect. Their stark beauty against the winter sky is a testament to the forest's resilience. They stand firm, weathering the winter's chill, their roots buried deep in the frozen earth, waiting patiently for the return of spring.

You find a space for introspection in the heart of the forest, surrounded by the silent serenity of snow-cloaked trees. The quietness allows your thoughts to flow freely, unencumbered by distractions. In its winter guise, the forest becomes a mirror, reflecting your inner self back to you.

Winter's hush is not a time of dormancy but rather a season of introspection and rejuvenation. It is a time to slow down, to breathe in the crisp air, to marvel at the beauty of the snow-cloaked trees, and to find peace in the forest's silent serenity. As you immerse yourself in this winter forest bathing experience, you become a part of the forest's quiet symphony, your heart beating in time with the silent rhythm of the winter woods.

Spring's Awakening: The Rebirth of Life

As winter's icy grip begins to loosen, the forest stirs from its slumber, heralding the arrival of spring. Spring is a tribute to this season of renewal, when the forest bathes itself in a fresh palette of vibrant hues, and the air is filled with the sweet perfume of blossoming flowers.

As you step into the forest during spring, you are greeted by a symphony of sounds. The once-silent woods are now alive with the melodious chirping of birds, the rustling of leaves, and the distant murmur of a babbling brook. The forest is celebrating the end of winter's reign and the arrival of a season of growth and rebirth.

Once bare and skeletal, the trees are now adorned with a lush canopy of leaves. The verdant foliage forms a natural cathedral, its arches reaching toward the sky, filtering the sunlight into a soft, mottled glow that dances on the forest floor. The sight is a feast for the eyes, a tableau of varying shades of green, from the pale, almost translucent hue of new leaves to the deep, rich color of mature foliage.

Beneath the towering trees, the forest floor is a carpet of wildflowers, their delicate petals unfurling to greet the sun. Each flower is a testament to the forest's resilience, a symbol of life's ability to endure even the harshest winters. As you walk amongst them, you can't help but feel a sense of awe and wonder at the sheer beauty of nature's handiwork.

Spring is also a time of activity for the forest's inhabitants. Squirrels scamper across the forest floor, their tiny paws leaving a trail in the soft, damp earth. Birds flit from branch to branch, their songs echoing through the trees. Deer graze peacefully in the clearings, their fawns taking their first tentative steps under the watchful eyes of their mothers.

Forest bathing in spring is a sensory experience, a chance to immerse yourself in the forest's sights, sounds, and smells. It is a time to slow down, to breathe in the fresh, crisp air, to listen to the rustling of leaves, to feel the warmth of the sun on your skin, and to marvel at the beauty of the forest in full bloom.

As you leave the forest, you carry with you a sense of peace and tranquility, a renewed appreciation for the simple beauty of nature, and a profound understanding of the cycle of life and renewal that the forest embodies. Spring's awakening is not just a season; it is a state of mind, a reminder of the endless cycle of life, death, and rebirth that is the essence of our existence.

Summer's Embrace: The Warm Whisper of Sun-Dappled Leaves

As the wheel of the year turns, the forest shifts from the vibrant rebirth of spring to the languid embrace of summer. The air is thick with sun-warmed pine and the sweet, heady perfume of blooming wildflowers. The forest is alive with a symphony of sounds, from the gentle rustle of leaves to the distant call of a bird. This is the season of summer's embrace, when the forest is lush and inviting, a time for the warm whisper of sun-dappled leaves.

The forest in summer is a place of abundance and vitality. The trees, now fully clothed in their verdant finery, stand tall and proud, their leaves a vibrant tapestry of greens. The sunlight filters through the canopy, casting a dotted pattern on the forest floor, a dance of light and shadow that changes with the passing hours. This is the forest's summer song, a melody composed of light, warmth, and the ceaseless rhythm of life.

Forest bathing in summer is a sensory feast. The touch of the warm breeze against your skin, the taste of sweet berries plucked straight from the bush, the sight of butterflies flitting among the flowers, the sound of leaves whispering secrets to each other as they sway in the wind, the scent of earth and leaves and life - all these combine to create an experience that is both grounding and uplifting.

Walking through the forest in summer, you can't help but feel a deep connection to the world around you. Each step takes you deeper into the heart of the forest; each breath draws the essence of summer into your being. Summer is a time for basking in the sun's warmth, lying on a bed of soft moss and watching the clouds drift by, and letting the forest's summer embrace wash over you and fill you with a sense of peace and contentment.

Summer's embrace is a time of growth and abundance, a time to celebrate the fullness of life. It is a time to immerse yourself in the forest's vibrant energy, to let the warm whisper of sun-dappled leaves guide you on your forest bathing journey. As you walk among the trees, let the forest's summer song fill your heart and soul and remind you of the beauty and wonder of the world around you. This is the magic of forest bathing in summer, which is there for all willing to open their hearts and minds to the forest's gentle embrace.

Autumn's Farewell: The Rustling Lullaby of Falling Foliage

As the year gently pivots towards its twilight, the forest begins to prepare for its grandest spectacle. Autumn, the season of mellow fruitfulness, arrives with a painter's palette, drenching the woodland in hues of gold, crimson, and amber. This time of the year invites you to immerse yourself in the forest's autumnal embrace when the trees bid farewell to their leafy crowns and the forest floor becomes a tapestry of fallen leaves.

The forest in autumn is a symphony of rustling leaves, a lullaby that sings of the year's maturity. Each leaf that falls is a note in this melody, a gentle reminder of the impermanence of life and the beauty of change. As you walk through the forest, the crunch of leaves underfoot and the whisper of the wind through the boughs create a soothing soundtrack, a natural music that invites introspection and tranquility.

The air in autumn carries a distinct crispness, a coolness that contrasts with the warmth of summer's lingering touch. It is a sensory delight, filled with the earthy scent of decaying leaves, the tang of ripening fruits, and the subtle hint of wood smoke from distant hearths. As you breathe in, you are not just inhaling air but the very essence of the forest, a blend of life, death, and rebirth that is as intoxicating as it is rejuvenating.

Forest bathing in autumn is a feast for the eyes. The trees, once a uniform green, now blaze with color, each one a testament to nature's artistry. The sunlight, softened by the shorter days, filters through the leaves, casting a golden glow that seems to set the forest alight. It is a breathtaking and humbling spectacle, a reminder of nature's ability to transform and renew.

As you immerse yourself in this autumnal wonderland, allow yourself to become a part of the forest's farewell. Feel the leaves crunch underfoot, listen to the rustling lullaby of the falling foliage, breathe in the crisp air, and let your eyes feast on the riot of colors. This is forest bathing at its most profound, a chance to connect with nature at a time of change and reflection when the forest prepares for the hush of winter in its quiet beautiful way.

Autumn's farewell is not an end but a transition, a pause before the cycle begins anew. It is a time to reflect, to appreciate, and to prepare. As the leaves fall and the forest quiets, we are reminded of the beauty of change, the inevitability of cycles, and the rejuvenating power of nature. So, as you walk through the autumn forest, let its rustling lullaby sooth your soul, and let its vibrant colors ignite your spirit. For in the heart of the forest, every season is a new beginning, and every farewell is but a prelude to a new hello.

The Ebb and Flow of Forest Bathing: Adapting to Change

Just as the forest breathes with the rhythm of the seasons, so should our practice of forest bathing adapt and flow with the changing times. Each season brings a unique palette of sensations, a distinct symphony of sounds, and a kaleidoscope of colors that can enrich our experience of the forest in profound ways.

In the heart of winter, when the forest is hushed under a blanket of snow, our forest bathing practice might take on a more contemplative tone. The silence of the snow-cloaked trees invites us to slow down, to listen more deeply, and to find peace in the stillness. We might choose to walk more slowly, to sit quietly by a frozen stream, or to stand in awe of the stark beauty of the winter landscape.

As spring unfurls its green tendrils, our forest bathing practice can awaken alongside the forest. The rebirth of life amidst the verdant canopies invites us to open our senses to the vibrant energy of growth and renewal. We may engage more actively with the forest, to touch the tender new leaves, to smell the fresh blossoms, or to listen to the chorus of birdsong.

In the embrace of summer, when the forest is dappled with warm sunlight, our forest bathing practice can become a celebration of abundance. The whisper of sun-dappled leaves invites us to bask in the joy of the present moment, feel the sun's warmth on our skin, and taste the sweet fruits of the season.

As autumn bids farewell, our forest bathing practice can become a gentle lullaby of letting go. The rustling of falling foliage invites us to reflect on the impermanence of life, appreciate the beauty of decay, and prepare for winter's stillness.

In this ebb and flow of forest bathing, we learn to adapt to the changing seasons, to honor the cycles of nature, and to find our place within the endless cycle of renewal and reflection. Just as the forest changes with the seasons, so too do we. And in this dance with the forest, we find a deeper connection to the world and the rhythms of our lives.

The Endless Cycle of Renewal and Reflection

As we draw the curtain on our year-long journey through the forest, we find ourselves standing at the threshold of a profound understanding. We have bathed in the forest's seasonal symphony; each note a whispering leaf, a rustling branch, a silent snowfall. We have learned to listen to the forest's heartbeat, to feel its pulse in the rhythm of the seasons. We have discovered that forest bathing is not merely a practice but a way of life, a way of being in harmony with the natural world.

Winter's hush taught us the beauty of silence and the serenity of solitude. We learned to appreciate the stark elegance of snow-cloaked trees, their bare branches reaching out to the grey skies like skeletal hands. We learned to find warmth in the cold and comfort in the quiet.

Spring's awakening brought us the rebirth of life and the resurgence of hope. We watched as the forest shook off its winter slumber as the verdant canopies unfurled their leaves to the sky. We learned to appreciate the miracle of growth, the magic of renewal.

Summer's embrace wrapped us in the warm whisper of sun-dappled leaves, the gentle hum of life in full bloom. We learned to appreciate nature's abundance and the earth's generosity.

Autumn's farewell sang us the rustling lullaby of falling foliage, the poignant beauty of endings. We learned to appreciate the cycle of life and the inevitability of change.

Through the ebb and flow of forest bathing, we have learned to adapt to the changing seasons to find peace in the constant flux of life. We have learned to breathe with the forest, to live with the forest, to be one with the forest.

As we conclude our year in the forest, we find ourselves not at the end but at the beginning of a new cycle. The forest has taught us that there are no true endings, only moments of reflection and renewal. We have learned to see each ending as a new beginning, each farewell as a new awakening.

In the forest, we have found a sanctuary of tranquility and rejuvenation. We have found a home. And as we step out of the forest, we carry its lessons with us, its wisdom etched into our hearts. We carry the forest within us, its rhythm pulsing in our veins, its melody humming in our souls.

And so, we bid farewell to the forest, not with a sense of loss but a sense of gratitude, for the forest has given us more than we could ever give back. It has given us a sense of belonging, a sense of peace, a sense of self. It has given us a year of memories and a lifetime of lessons.

And as we step into the new year, we step with the forest. We step with the seasons. We step with the rhythm of life. We step into the endless cycle of renewal and reflection. We step with the forest, and the forest steps with us.

Chapter Summary

- The forest's seasonal symphony is a testament to its resilience and adaptability, with each season offering a unique backdrop for the practice of forest bathing.
- The practice of forest bathing should adapt and flow with the changing seasons, each offering a unique palette of sensations, sounds, and colors that can enrich the experience of the forest.
- Winter's hush invites introspection and peace, with the silent serenity of snow-cloaked trees offering a space for contemplation and rejuvenation.
- Spring's awakening is a sensory experience filled with the vibrant energy of growth and renewal, offering a chance to immerse oneself in the forest's sights, sounds, and smells in full bloom.

- Summer's embrace celebrates abundance and vitality, with the warm whisper of sun-dappled leaves providing a grounding and uplifting forest bathing experience.
- Autumn's farewell is a gentle lullaby of letting go, with the rustling of falling foliage inviting reflection on the impermanence of life and the beauty of change.
- Forest bathing is not merely a practice but a way of life, a way of being in harmony with the natural world and learning to adapt to the changing seasons, honor the cycles of nature, and find our place within the endless cycle of renewal and reflection.
- The forest offers a sanctuary, a place of tranquility and rejuvenation, and through the practice of forest bathing, we can carry its lessons and wisdom with us, finding a sense of belonging, peace, and self.

8

FOREST BATHING WITH CHILDREN: CULTIVATING A LOVE FOR NATURE

A world of wonder awaits in the peaceful tranquility of the forest. This world, teeming with life and mystery, holds a special allure for children. Their eyes light up with curiosity and delight as they explore, their senses awakened by the forest's myriad sights, sounds, and scents. This is the joy of introducing children to forest bathing. This practice immerses them in nature's beauty and nurtures their physical, emotional, and cognitive development.

Forest bathing is not about hiking or exercising but about being present, slowing down, and allowing the forest to envelop you, speaking to you in its quiet, serene language. It is about letting the forest air, filled with the soothing scent of pine and earth, cleanse your spirit and rejuvenate your senses.

Introducing children to forest bathing is akin to opening the door to a magical realm where they can touch the rough bark of a tree, listen to the whispering wind, watch a squirrel scamper up a branch, and feel the cool forest floor beneath their feet. It is a realm where they can learn, grow, and form a deep, lasting bond with nature.

The joy of introducing children to forest bathing lies in the immediate happiness and excitement it brings them and the long-term benefits it offers. It is a joy that stems from knowing that you are giving them a gift that will enrich their lives and help them become more mindful, more respectful of nature, and more in tune with their own senses and emotions.

As we journey through this chapter, we will explore the importance of nature for a child's development, how to prepare for your first forest bathing experience with children, engaging activities to enhance the experience, and ways to nurture mindfulness and respect for nature in children. We will delve into the transformative impact of regular forest bathing on children and how it can foster a lifelong bond with nature.

So, let us embark on this journey, hand in hand with our children, and step into the tranquil embrace of the forest. Let us introduce them to the joy of forest bathing and cultivate a love for nature that will nourish their souls and enrich their lives.

The Importance of Nature for a Child's Development

In the gentle hush of the forest, where sunlight filters through the canopy and the air is imbued with the scent of earth and leaves, a child's development finds a nurturing cradle. In its raw and unfiltered form, nature is a profound teacher, a silent guide, and a playground that fosters growth in ways that the confines of concrete walls and digital screens cannot.

The forest, with its myriad of life forms, textures, sounds, and smells, stimulates a child's senses in a holistic and balanced manner. The rustle of leaves underfoot, the whisper of the wind through the trees, the sight of a squirrel darting up a trunk, the feel of bark under tiny fingers, the taste of wild berries - all these experiences awaken and engage a child's senses, fostering a keen awareness of their surroundings.

In the heart of nature, children learn to appreciate the beauty of simplicity. They discover joy in the smallest things - a fallen leaf, a smooth pebble, a bird's song. This appreciation for simplicity cultivates a sense of contentment and gratitude, qualities that are essential for emotional well-being.

The forest also provides a rich platform for cognitive development

Children learn to recognize patterns and sequences in nature, enhancing their problem-solving skills. They develop spatial awareness as they navigate the woods, and their curiosity is piqued as they explore and make discoveries, fostering a love for learning.

Moreover, the forest is where children can experience freedom and autonomy. They can run, climb, hide, and explore at their own pace, in their own way. This freedom to explore and make decisions enhances their self-confidence and decision-making skills.

In the tranquility of the forest, children also learn the art of mindfulness. They learn to be present, listen, observe, and breathe. This mindfulness reduces stress and anxiety and enhances focus and concentration.

Lastly, children develop a deep-rooted respect and love for the environment by spending time in nature. They learn about the delicate balance of ecosystems, the importance of conservation, and the joy of co-existing with other life forms. This understanding fosters a sense of responsibility and stewardship for the earth, shaping them into conscious and caring adults.

The forest is a nurturing ground for a child's physical, cognitive, emotional, and social development. It is a place where children can grow, learn, and flourish most naturally and joyfully.

Preparing for Your First Forest Bathing Experience with Children

As the sun peeks over the horizon, casting a soft, golden glow on the dew-kissed leaves, you find yourself standing at the edge of the forest, your child's hand nestled warmly in your own. The air is crisp and clean, with the scent of damp earth and wildflowers' faint, sweet perfume. This is the moment you've been waiting for: your first forest bathing experience with children.

Preparing for this experience is not merely about packing the right snacks or dressing in suitable attire, though these practicalities are essential. It is about setting the stage for a journey of discovery that will awaken your child's senses, ignite their curiosity, and foster a deep, enduring love for nature.

Begin by choosing a day when you both are free from obligations. Forest bathing is not an activity to be rushed; it is a slow, deliberate immersion into the natural world. Choose a forest that is safe and accessible, but also rich in biodiversity. The more variety in flora and fauna, the more engaging the experience will be for your child.

Before you set foot in the forest, take a moment to explain to your child what forest bathing is. Use simple, clear language that they can understand. You might say, "We're going on a special adventure in the forest today. We're not going to walk fast or try to get anywhere. We're just going to be in the forest, looking, listening, and feeling. It's like taking a bath in the forest, but we're bathing our senses, not our bodies."

Encourage your child to leave their toys and gadgets behind. This is a time for them to engage directly with nature, unmediated by screens or artificial distractions. Instead, equip them with a magnifying glass, a notebook, and colored pencils for drawing what they observe.

Dress appropriately for the weather and the terrain. Comfortable, sturdy shoes are a must, as are clothes that can get a little dirty. After all, the best forest bathing experiences often involve a bit of mud and leaf litter!

Finally, set some ground rules to ensure safety and respect for nature. Remind your child to stay close, to avoid disturbing wildlife, and to leave no trace behind.

As you prepare for this first forest bathing experience with your child, remember that the goal is not to 'do' but to 'be.' It is about being present, being curious, and being open to the wonders that nature has to offer. It is about cultivating a love for nature that will, with hope and care, grow and flourish in your child's heart, just like the mighty trees in the forest you are about to explore.

Engaging Activities to Enhance the Forest Bathing Experience

As the forest unfurls its verdant arms, welcoming you and your little ones into its tranquil embrace, it's time to explore the myriad of engaging activities that can enhance your forest bathing experience. These activities are about keeping children entertained and fostering a deep, meaningful connection with nature that will nourish their souls and ignite their curiosity.

Begin with a simple sensory exploration. Encourage your children to close their eyes and tune into the sounds of the forest. The rustling leaves whispering ancient tales, the bird's distant call, the wind's soft sigh - all these sounds create a soothing melody that can calm the busiest of minds. Ask them to touch a tree's rough bark, feel the coolness of a leaf, or the delicate softness of a mossy patch. Each texture tells a story, and each sensation is a thread in the intricate tapestry of the forest.

Next, engage their sense of smell. The forest is a treasure trove of natural aromas. The earthy scent of the soil, the fresh fragrance of pine needles, the sweet perfume of wildflowers - each inhalation is a step deeper into the heart of the forest. This olfactory exploration enhances their sensory experience and helps them develop a keen awareness of their surroundings.

A scavenger hunt is another delightful activity that can add a dash of adventure to your forest bathing experience. Create a list of natural items for them to find - a feather, a pinecone, a smooth stone, or a leaf of a specific shape. This sharpens their observation skills and encourages them to interact with the forest respectfully and mindfully.

Introduce them to the art of forest journaling. Provide them with a notebook and some colored pencils, and encourage them to sketch what they see, write about their feelings, or jot down the sounds they hear. This practice nurtures their creativity and helps them healthily process their experiences and emotions.

Lastly, engage them in the simple joy of quiet contemplation. Find a comfortable spot, perhaps under the shade of a towering tree or by a babbling brook, and encourage them to sit quietly, observe, breathe, and be. This mindfulness practice, being fully present in the moment, is one of the most precious gifts that forest bathing can offer.

These activities, woven into the fabric of your forest bathing experience, can transform a simple walk in the woods into a magical journey of discovery, learning, and growth. They can help your children cultivate a deep love for nature, a love that will guide them, inspire them, and nourish them throughout their lives.

Nurturing Mindfulness and Respect for Nature in Children

A child can learn to be genuinely present in the heart of the forest, where the air is pure, and the silence is punctuated only by the rustling of leaves and the songs of birds. This is the essence of mindfulness - the ability to fully engage in the here and now, be aware of one's surroundings and appreciate the beauty of the moment. Forest bathing provides an ideal setting for nurturing this quality in children.

Begin by encouraging your child to close their eyes and take a deep breath, inhaling the scent of the forest. Ask them to focus on the sensation of the air entering their lungs, the feeling of the earth beneath their feet, and the sun's warmth on their skin. This simple exercise can help them tune into their senses and become more aware of their connection to the natural world.

Next, invite them to open their eyes and look at the forest around them. Encourage them to notice the different shades of green, the patterns of light and shadow, and how the leaves move in the breeze. Ask them to listen to the sounds of the forest - the rustling of leaves, the chirping of birds, the distant murmur of a stream. This can help them develop a deeper appreciation for the beauty and complexity of nature.

Teaching children to respect nature is another crucial aspect of forest bathing. This can be as simple as reminding them not to litter, to stay on the trails, and to avoid disturbing the wildlife. But it can also involve more profound lessons about the interconnectedness of all living things and the importance of preserving the natural world for future generations.

One effective way to foster this respect is by involving children in conservation activities, such as planting trees or cleaning up litter. This can help them understand that they have a role in protecting the environment and that their actions can make a difference.

In the tranquility of the forest, children can learn to be mindful, to appreciate the beauty of nature, and to respect the environment. These valuable lessons can enrich their lives and help them grow into responsible, caring adults. In the process, they will also discover a lifelong love for nature and a sense of peace and joy they can carry wherever they go.

The Transformative Impact of Regular Forest Bathing on Children

Regular forest bathing, a practice steeped in simplicity and profound impact, can be a transformative experience for children, shaping their relationship with nature and themselves.

The forest is a living, breathing classroom where every leaf, every stone, every creature has a story to tell. As children immerse themselves in this natural wonder, they learn to observe, question, and explore. They learn about the interconnectedness of life, the delicate balance that sustains it, and their role within this grand tapestry. This understanding fosters a sense of responsibility, a respect for nature that transcends the superficial and seeps into their very being.

The forest also teaches children about the rhythms of life, the ebb and flow of seasons, and the cycle of growth and decay. In this ever-changing yet constant environment, children learn to appreciate the beauty of transience, the value of patience, and the virtue of resilience. They learn that, like the forest, they can weather storms and bloom anew.

Moreover, forest bathing is a journey into the self. As children wander amidst the trees, they also navigate the landscape of their emotions, thoughts, and dreams. With its tranquil solitude, the forest provides a safe space for introspection and self-discovery. It encourages children to listen to their inner voice, trust their instincts, and believe in their potential.

The impact of regular forest bathing on children is not just immediate but enduring. It shapes their perspective, their values, and their behavior. It instills in them a love for nature that is not just an interest but a way of life. It equips them with the tools to lead a mindful, balanced, and fulfilling life.

In the end, forest bathing is more than just a walk in the woods. It invites children to embrace the world with open hearts and curious minds. It is a promise of a lifelong bond with nature, a bond that nurtures them, inspires them, and guides them on their journey through life.

Fostering a Lifelong Bond with Nature through Forest Bathing

As the sun sets on our journey through the verdant realm of forest bathing with children, we find ourselves standing at the threshold of a new dawn. A dawn where our children, imbued with a profound love for nature, step forward to become the stewards of our planet. This is the transformative power of forest bathing, a practice that rejuvenates the senses and fosters a lifelong bond with nature.

The forest, with its towering trees, rustling leaves, and the symphony of birdsong, is a living, breathing classroom. Here, children learn the language of the wind, the secrets of the soil, and the stories written in the stars. Each forest bathing experience is a chapter in their lifelong journey of discovery, a journey that nurtures their curiosity, creativity, and compassion.

As we guide our children through this journey, we are not merely teaching them to appreciate the beauty of nature. We are helping them understand their place in the grand tapestry of life. We show them that they are not separate from nature but integral to it. This understanding, this sense of interconnectedness, is the foundation of a deep and enduring love for nature.

Forest bathing is not a one-time event but a continuous process of growth and transformation. Each visit to the forest is an opportunity to deepen our connection with nature, to learn from its wisdom, and to be healed by its tranquility. As our children grow, so too does their bond with the forest. It becomes a sanctuary of peace in a chaotic world, a source of inspiration in times of doubt, and a wellspring of joy in moments of celebration.

In conclusion, forest bathing with children is a journey of the heart, a dance of the soul, and a celebration of life. It is a gift that we give our children, a gift they will carry with them long after they have grown

We plant a seed of love in their hearts, a seed that will grow into a mighty tree deeply rooted in the soil of respect and reverence for nature.

As we step out of the forest, we carry with us the whispers of the wind, the birds' songs, and the earth's fragrance. We carry the memories of shared laughter, wonder, and silence. But most importantly, we promise a brighter future, where our children, bathed in the light of love for nature, lead the way towards a more harmonious and sustainable world.

Chapter Summary

- Forest bathing can be a transformative experience for children, nurturing their physical, emotional, and cognitive development.
- The forest, with its myriad of life forms, textures, sounds, and smells, stimulates a child's senses in a holistic and balanced manner, fostering a keen awareness of their surroundings and a deep-rooted respect and love for the environment.
- Preparing for a forest bathing experience with children involves choosing a suitable day and location, explaining the concept in simple terms, and setting ground rules for safety and respect for nature.
- Engaging in sensory exploration, scavenger hunts, forest journaling, and quiet contemplation can enhance the forest bathing experience, fostering a deep, meaningful connection with nature.
- Forest bathing provides an ideal setting for nurturing mindfulness in children, teaching them to be fully engaged in the here and now, aware of their surroundings, and appreciate the beauty of the moment.
- Regular forest bathing can transform children, shaping their relationship with nature and themselves, fostering a sense of

responsibility and respect for nature, and equipping them with the tools to lead a mindful, balanced, and fulfilling life.

- Forest bathing is a continuous process of growth and transformation; each visit to the forest deepens the child's connection with nature, and as they grow, so does their bond with the forest.
- Forest bathing with children is a journey of the heart, a dance of the soul, and a celebration of life. It is a gift that we give to our children, a gift that they will carry with them long after they have grown, deeply rooted in the soil of respect and reverence for nature.

9

FOREST BATHING IN URBAN SPACES: FINDING YOUR GREEN OASIS

The quest for green can seem daunting in the heart of the city, where steel and concrete reign supreme. The urban landscape, with its towering skyscrapers and bustling streets, often leaves little room for the tranquil embrace of nature. Yet, amidst the relentless hum of city life, there exists a quiet yearning for the soothing whispers of the wind, the gentle rustle of leaves, and the calming rhythm of life that pulses in the forest's heart. This is the quest for green in the concrete jungle, a journey towards finding your oasis of tranquility amidst the urban chaos.

For all its vibrancy and dynamism, the city can often feel overwhelming. The constant rush, the ceaseless noise, and the ever-present pressure can take a toll on the most resilient spirits. In such times, the soul seeks solace, a place of quiet where one can reconnect with oneself and the world around. This is where the concept of forest bathing comes into play.

Forest bathing is not about hiking or jogging through a forest. It is about immersing oneself in the forest atmosphere, about letting the forest in. It is about taking the time to slow down, breathe in the fresh air, listen to the subtle symphony of nature, and let the forest cleanse your mind and rejuvenate your spirit.

But how does one embark on this journey of forest bathing in the heart of the city? How does one find a green oasis amidst the concrete and steel? This chapter aims to guide you on this journey, to help you discover your own urban green spaces where you can practice forest bathing and find a moment of peace amidst the urban hustle.

The quest for green in the concrete jungle is not just a journey toward finding a physical space. It is a journey towards finding a state of mind, peace, and tranquility that comes from being in harmony with nature, even in the most unlikely places. It is about finding a way to bring the forest to the city, creating a space where the soul can breathe freely, the mind can find respite, and the spirit can soar.

So, let us embark on this journey together. Let us explore the concept of urban forest bathing and discover how to find our own green oasis in the heart of the concrete jungle.

Urban Forest Bathing: A Breath of Fresh Air

In the heart of the city, where steel and concrete reign supreme, the concept of forest bathing may seem like a distant dream, a luxury reserved for those who can escape to the countryside. Yet, the essence of forest bathing is not confined to the wilderness. It is a practice that can be embraced anywhere, even amidst the urban sprawl.

Urban forest bathing is the art of finding tranquility and rejuvenation in our cities' green spaces. It is about immersing oneself in the presence of trees, plants, and the open sky, even if skyscrapers surround them. It is about seeking solace in the rustle of leaves, the chirping of birds, the whisper of the wind, and the dance of sunlight through the foliage, all within the confines of the city.

This concept is not about the size of the green space or the number of trees it houses. It is about the quality of the connection that one can forge with nature in these spaces. A single tree in a busy street, a small park tucked away in a residential area, a rooftop garden, or even a balcony filled with potted plants can serve as an oasis for urban forest bathing.

Urban forest bathing is a reminder that nature is not separate from us but exists only in remote locations. It is all around us, even in the most urbanized settings. It is a call to slow down, breathe, observe, and connect with the natural world amid our hectic city lives.

The concept of urban forest bathing is a breath of fresh air because it offers a way to experience the healing power of nature without leaving the city. It is a practice that can be woven into the fabric of our daily lives, a practice that can make our cities feel a little less grey and a little more green. It is a practice that can help us find balance, peace, and rejuvenation, even in the heart of the concrete jungle.

Identifying Potential Green Oases: Your Urban Forest Bathing Spots

The quest for a green oasis might seem daunting in the heart of the city, where steel and concrete dominate the landscape. Yet, even in the most urbanized environments, nature persists, carving out pockets of tranquility amidst the hustle and bustle. These are your potential urban forest bathing spots, your green oases, waiting to be discovered and cherished.

Begin your search by opening your senses to the world around you. Listen for the rustle of leaves, the chirping of birds, the whisper of wind through the branches. Look for the subtle shades of green that break the monotony of the cityscape. Smell the earthy scent of soil after a rain, the sweet fragrance of blooming flowers, and the fresh aroma of dew-kissed grass. Feel the rough bark of a tree, the softness of moss, the coolness of a leaf's shade. Taste the crispness of the air after a storm, the sweetness of a ripe berry, the tang of a leaf's sap.

Parks are the most obvious choice for urban forest bathing. They are designed to be green spaces where nature is nurtured and protected. Seek out the quiet corners, the secluded spots, the areas where the trees grow thick, and the grass runs wild.

But don't limit yourself to parks. Look for other green spaces that might be overlooked. A tree-lined street, a rooftop garden, a courtyard filled with plants, and a riverbank teeming with life can all serve as your urban forest bathing spots.

Community gardens are another excellent option. They are green spaces and social spaces where you can connect with others who share your love for nature. Participating in a community garden can deepen your forest bathing experience, adding a layer of community and camaraderie to the tranquility and rejuvenation.

Even the smallest patch of green can serve as an urban forest bathing spot. A single tree can be a source of calm and comfort, a place to rest and recharge. A cluster of potted plants can be a mini forest, a tiny oasis in the concrete desert.

Remember, the goal of forest bathing is not to find the most spectacular or pristine natural setting but to connect with nature deeply and meaningfully. Even in the city's heart, you can find your green oasis, your sanctuary of serenity and peace. So, step out of your door, open your senses, and let the city reveal its hidden green treasures.

Techniques for Forest Bathing in Urban Spaces

Even amidst the grey, there are pockets of green waiting to be discovered and bathed in. Forest bathing in urban spaces is not just possible; it is a necessity, a balm for the weary urban soul. Here, we delve into the techniques to help you embrace the green amidst the grey.

The first step is to find your green oasis. It could be a park, a community garden, a tree-lined street, or even a balcony filled with potted plants. The size of the space does not matter as much as the quality of you engagement with it. Once you have found your green oasis, make it point to visit it regularly. The more familiar you become with the space the deeper your connection will be.

When you step into your green oasis, leave behind the hustle an bustle of the city. Leave behind your worries, your to-do lists, and you deadlines. This is a time for you to be present and in the moment. As yo enter the space, take a deep breath. Let the air fill your lungs; let the scer of the greenery fill your senses. This is the beginning of your urban forest bathing experience.

Walk slowly, mindfully. Feel the ground beneath your feet, the breeze on your skin. Listen to the rustle of the leaves, the birds chirping, and the insects' hum. Look at the different shades of green, the patterns of the leaves, and how the sunlight filters through the branches. Touch the bark of the trees, the petals of the flowers, and the grass blades. Each of these actions helps you connect with nature and helps you immerse yourself in the experience.

As you walk, practice mindful breathing. Inhale deeply, exhale slowly. With each breath, imagine that you are drawing in the energy of the forest, the vitality of the green. With each exhale, imagine that you are releasing stress and negativity. This is not just a physical exercise. It is a spiritual one, a way of cleansing your spirit, of rejuvenating your soul.

Remember, there is no right or wrong way to forest bathe. The most important thing is to be open and receptive. Let nature guide you; let your instincts guide you. You may find that you are drawn to a particular tree or spot. Follow that instinct. Sit under the tree, lie on the grass, close your eyes, and let your mind wander. This is your time, your space, your moment of tranquility amidst the chaos of the city.

Forest bathing in urban spaces is not just about finding a green oasis. It is about creating one within yourself. It is about finding peace, balance, and belonging in an overwhelming world. So, embrace the green amidst the grey, immerse yourself in the experience, and let the forest bathe you in its healing, rejuvenating energy.

Case Studies: Urban Forest Bathing Experiences

In the city's heart, where the hum of traffic is a constant companion, and skyscrapers reach for the heavens, it may seem impossible to find a tranquil, green oasis. Yet, many have found such spaces and successfully embraced the practice of forest bathing within them. Let us delve into the experiences of these urban dwellers, who have discovered the art of finding serenity amidst the city's chaos.

Case Study 1

Our first case study takes us to the bustling city of New York, where the iconic Central Park serves as a green lung amidst the concrete landscape. Here, we meet Anna, a corporate lawyer who has made forest bathing a part of her daily routine. Before the city fully awakens every morning, she walks on the dew-kissed grass, allowing the cool sensation to seep into her being. She breathes in the fresh air, subtly scented with the earthy aroma of damp soil and the sweet fragrance of blooming flowers. Anna shares that this practice has reduced her stress levels and made her more mindful and appreciative of the natural beauty that exists even in the heart of the city.

Case Study 2

Next, we travel to Tokyo, the city that gave birth to the concept of forest bathing or 'Shinrin-yoku.' Amidst the neon lights and towering buildings, we find the tranquil Meiji Shrine forest. Here, we meet Takana, a tech entrepreneur who has found solace in this urban forest's dense, verdant foliage. He spends his weekends here, immersing himself in the sounds of rustling leaves, chirping birds, and the sight of sunlight filtering through the canopy. Takana believes that forest bathing has improved his mental health and inspired creativity in his work.

Case Study 3

Our final case study brings us to London, where the sprawling Hyde Park offers a green retreat to city dwellers. Here, we meet Emma, a university student who has found a unique way to combine her studies with forest bathing. She often sits by the Serpentine Lake, reading amidst the gentle rustle of leaves and the soft lapping of water against the shore. Emma shares that this practice has helped her focus better on her studies and instilled a deep sense of calm and peace.

These stories testify to the transformative power of forest bathing, even in the most unlikely places. They remind us that nature is not confined to remote forests or mountain tops but can be found in the heart of our cities, waiting to offer us a moment of tranquility and rejuvenation.

The Impact of Urban Forest Bathing

In the city's heart, where the hum of traffic and the rhythm of urban life are constant companions, forest bathing may seem like a distant dream. Yet, as we have explored, engaging in this practice within the confines of our urban landscapes is not only possible but also profoundly beneficial. The impact of urban forest bathing, both on a personal and environmental level, is a testament to the resilience of nature and the human spirit's innate connection to it.

On a personal level, urban forest bathing offers a sanctuary of serenity amidst the urban chaos. It is a gentle reminder that tranquility can be found even in the most unexpected places. The rustle of leaves underfoot, the dappled sunlight filtering through the branches, the scent of damp earth after a rain shower - these sensory experiences serve as a balm for the weary urban soul. They ground us, reminding us of our inherent connection to the natural world, a connection often forgotten in the hustle and bustle of city life.

Forest bathing in urban spaces also fosters mindfulness, a state of being fully present and engaged in the current moment. As we navigate the green oases within our concrete jungles, we become more attuned to the subtle changes in our environment - the shifting patterns of light and shadow, the changing seasons reflected in the foliage, and the quiet inhabitants of these urban forests. This heightened awareness extends beyond our forest bathing sessions, influencing our daily interactions and experiences.

From an environmental perspective, urban forest bathing underscores the importance of preserving and nurturing green spaces within our cities. These green oases serve as vital lungs for our urban environments, absorbing carbon dioxide, filtering pollutants, and providing a habitat for various flora and fauna. They are a testament to the resilience of nature, flourishing amidst concrete and steel.

Moreover, as more individuals engage in urban forest bathing, there is a growing recognition of the value of these green spaces. This awareness can translate into action, inspiring urban planning policies that prioritize creating and preserving green spaces. It can also foster a sense of community stewardship, encouraging city dwellers to care for their local green oases actively.

In conclusion, the impact of urban forest bathing is far-reaching, touching both the personal and environmental spheres. It is a practice that nurtures the human spirit, fosters mindfulness, and promotes environmental stewardship. As we continue to navigate the complexities of urban life, these green oases remind us of the tranquility and rejuvenation that nature offers, even in the heart of the concrete jungle.

The Future of Forest Bathing in Urban Spaces

As our journey through the verdant labyrinth of urban forest bathing draws close, we find ourselves standing on the precipice of a future where the green and the grey coexist in harmonious balance. The future of forest bathing in urban spaces is not a distant dream but a tangible reality slowly unfurling its emerald tendrils in the heart of our concrete jungles.

The cityscape, often perceived as a monotonous expanse of steel and stone, is gradually reimagined as a canvas where the vibrant strokes of nature can be artfully woven into the urban fabric. Forest bathing in urban spaces is gaining momentum, not just as a wellness trend but as a transformative lifestyle that encourages a deeper connection with the natural world, even within the confines of our bustling metropolises.

As we move forward, the potential for urban forest bathing is immense. The green oases we have identified and explored can multiply, sprouting in every corner of our cities, from the smallest pocket parks to the expansive urban forests. These spaces can serve as sanctuaries where city dwellers can retreat to immerse themselves in the soothing balm of nature, breathe in the verdant air, and let the tranquility of the forest seep into their beings.

The techniques we have discussed for forest bathing in urban spaces will continue to evolve, adapting to each city's unique challenges and opportunities. The experiences shared in our case studies serve as a testament to the transformative power of urban forest bathing, and we hope that they inspire countless more such experiences.

From a personal perspective, urban forest bathing can become vital for stress management, mental clarity, and overall well-being. From an environmental perspective, the rise of urban forest bathing can foster a greater appreciation for our urban green spaces, leading to more concerted conservation efforts and sustainable urban planning.

In conclusion, the future of forest bathing in urban spaces is a vision of cities where the green and the grey dance in a harmonious ballet, where the rustle of leaves is a familiar soundtrack, and where every city dweller can experience the profound tranquility of forest bathing. It is a future where our cities are not just habitats but sanctuaries of well-being, where the healing power of nature is just a few steps away, waiting to be discovered in our green oases.

Chapter Summary

- The quest for green in the concrete jungle is a journey toward finding tranquility amidst urban chaos. This is achieved through forest bathing, which involves immersing oneself in the forest atmosphere to rejuvenate the spirit.
- Urban forest bathing is the art of finding tranquility in the green spaces within cities. It involves seeking solace in the presence of trees, plants, and the open sky, even if surrounded by skyscrapers.
- Identifying potential green oases in the city involves opening your senses to the world. Parks, tree-lined streets, rooftop

gardens, courtyards filled with plants, and riverbanks teeming with life can all serve as urban forest bathing spots.

- Techniques for forest bathing in urban spaces involve finding and visiting a green oasis regularly, walking slowly and mindfully, practicing mindful breathing, and allowing nature and your instincts to guide you.
- The impact of urban forest bathing is profound on both a personal and environmental level. It offers a sanctuary of serenity, fosters mindfulness, underscores the importance of preserving green spaces, and promotes environmental stewardship.
- The future of forest bathing in urban spaces is promising. The concept is gaining momentum and has the potential to transform cities into sanctuaries of well-being where the healing power of nature is accessible to all city dwellers.
- Urban forest bathing can improve stress management, mental clarity, and well-being. It can also foster a greater appreciation for urban green spaces, leading to more concerted conservation efforts and sustainable urban planning.

10

TRANSFORMATIVE EXPERIENCES OF FOREST BATHING

In its timeless wisdom, the forest offers a gentle refuge from the clamor of our daily lives. It is a testament to resilience and growth, its towering trees reaching the sky in a silent symphony of life. Here, amidst the rustling leaves and the soft hum of life, we find a space to reconnect with our inner selves, heal, and rejuvenate.

Forest bathing is an intimate communion with nature, a mindful immersion into the forest's soothing balm. It is a practice that encourages us to slow down, listen to the whispers of the wind, feel the cool touch of moss under our fingertips, and gaze upon the intricate patterns of leaves and bark. In these moments of quiet contemplation, we begin to understand the profound healing power of the forest.

The anecdotes that follow in this chapter illustrate experiences you may encounter in your forest bathing journey, as well as narratives of individuals who have experienced the transformative power of forest bathing. They speak of awakenings and profound revelations, sensory experiences that have stirred souls, and the lasting impressions the forest has left upon hearts. These are experiences of renewal and transformation, the resurgence of hope, and the enduring call of the forest.

As you journey through these narratives, may you find inspiration and solace in the experiences of others. May you step into the forest's healing embrace, breathe in its tranquility, and allow its energy to rejuvenate your spirit. For in the heart of the forest, there is a serenity waiting to welcome you, a sanctuary where you can find healing, peace, and a profound connection with the natural world.

The Awakening: A First Encounter with Forest Bathing

The story begins with awakening in the forest's heart, where the sunlight filters through the verdant canopy, casting dappled shadows on the forest floor. It is a tale not of grand adventures or epic quests but of a quiet, profound encounter with the natural world. It is the story of the first experience of forest bathing.

Imagine stepping into the forest, leaving behind the clamor of the everyday world. The air is cool and fresh, filled with the scent of damp earth and the subtle perfume of wildflowers. The only sounds are the rustling of leaves in the breeze, the distant call of a bird, and the soft crunch of your footsteps on the forest floor. It is a world apart, a sanctuary of tranquility and peace.

As you walk deeper into the forest, you feel a sense of calm washing over you. The worries and stresses of life seem to fall away, replaced by a feeling of serenity and contentment. You are not merely in the forest; you are a part of it, connected to it profoundly and intimately.

You begin to notice things you might have overlooked before: the intricate patterns of bark on a tree trunk, the delicate beauty of a single leaf, and the way the light dances on the surface of a stream. You feel the coolness of the earth beneath your feet, the sun's warmth on your skin, and the gentle caress of the breeze. You breathe deeply, filling your lungs with pure, clean air.

This is the awakening, the first encounter with forest bathing. It is a moment of revelation, a realization of the deep connection between yourself and the natural world. It is a feeling of being fully present, fully alive fully human.

At this moment, you understand what it means to bathe in the forest to immerse yourself in nature, to let it wash over you and cleanse you, body and soul. You feel a sense of peace and tranquility you have never known before, a sense of being at one with the world around you.

This is the beginning of a journey of discovery and transformation. It is a journey that will take you deeper into the heart of the forest and the heart of yourself. It is a journey that begins with a single step, breath, and moment of awakening.

The Journey Within: Profound Revelations Amidst the Trees

The forest is a stage for the journey within, a transformative process that unfolds as one immerses oneself in the serene embrace of the forest.

The journey begins with a single step: a conscious decision to leave behind the clamor of the outside world and step into the tranquil realm of the forest. As the forest bathers recounted, this initial step was often accompanied by a sense of trepidation, a fear of the unknown. Yet, as they ventured deeper into the forest, this fear gradually gave way to a sense of peace and tranquility.

With its timeless wisdom, the forest has a way of peeling back the layers of our consciousness, revealing the core of our being. Amidst the towering trees and the gentle rustle of leaves, bathers confronted their deepest fears, unfulfilled dreams, and most cherished hopes. In its silent eloquence, the forest provided a safe space for these revelations to surface, allowing the bathers to acknowledge and confront these hidden aspects of themselves.

One bather recounted how, in the serenity of the forest, she found the courage to face a painful memory that she had long suppressed. As she sat beneath a towering pine, she felt a surge of emotion well up within her. She allowed herself to feel the pain, cry, and eventually let go. In its infinite compassion, the forest bore witness to her pain and provided solace in its tranquil embrace.

Another bather spoke of a profound realization that dawned upon him as he watched a leaf gently fall to the ground. He realized the impermanence of life and the importance of living in the present moment. This revelation, he shared, transformed his perspective on life and instilled a deep sense of peace.

These stories of profound revelations amidst the trees testify to the transformative power of forest bathing. With its serene beauty and timeless wisdom, the forest invites us on a journey that leads to self-discovery, healing, and transformation. As we immerse ourselves in the tranquil embrace of the forest, we embark on a journey of self-discovery that leads us back to our true selves.

The Symphony of Nature: Sensory Experiences in Forest Bathing

In the heart of the forest, a symphony of nature unfolds. The concert requires no ticket, no grand hall, only an open heart and a willingness to listen. The forest is a maestro, conducting a harmonious orchestra of sights, sounds, scents, and sensations that awaken the senses and soothe the soul.

Imagine standing amidst the towering trees, their leaves whispering secrets in the gentle breeze. The rustle of foliage is a soft lullaby, a soothing serenade that invites you to let go of your worries and surrender to the rhythm of nature. The forest floor, a carpet of moss and fallen leaves, crunches softly underfoot, a tactile reminder of the life beneath the surface.

The air is alive with pine and damp earth, a heady perfume that fills the lungs and cleanses the spirit. The forest is a sensory feast, a banquet of natural wonders that nourishes the soul. Each breath is a sip of pure, unfiltered air, each step a taste of nature's wild, untamed beauty.

The forest is a canvas of colors, a masterpiece painted by the hand of Mother Nature. The vibrant green of the leaves, the rich brown of the bark, the delicate hues of wildflowers that dot the landscape - each detail is a brushstroke in this breathtaking tableau. The sunlight filters through the canopy, casting dappled shadows that dance and play on the forest floor.

And then there are the sounds - the chirping of birds, the rustling of leaves, the distant murmur of a babbling brook. Each note is a part of the forest's symphony, a melody that resonates in the heart and echoes in the soul.

Forest bathing is not merely a walk in the woods. It is an immersive experience, a sensory journey that invites you to connect profoundly with nature. It is a symphony of nature, a concert that plays on the soul's strings and leaves a melody that lingers long after the forest fades from view.

In the embrace of the forest, we find a sanctuary, a place of peace and tranquility where the symphony of nature plays on an endless loop. It is here, amidst the trees, that we find ourselves, our senses awakened, our spirits rejuvenated. The forest is not just a place but a state of being, a symphony that plays in the heart of every forest bather.

The Resurgence: Stories of Renewal and Transformation

In the heart of the forest, where the air is thick with the scent of pine and the whispers of the wind, a profound resurgence occurs. It is a rebirth, a renewal, a transformation that is as tangible as the bark of the trees and as ethereal as the dappled sunlight filtering through the leaves.

One such story of resurgence is that of Maria, a woman who found herself lost in the labyrinth of life. She was trapped in the relentless pace of the modern world, her spirit dulled by the monotony of routine. It was in the forest that Maria found her way back to herself. As she immersed herself in the verdant embrace of the trees, she felt a shift within her. With its timeless wisdom and tranquil beauty, the forest began to heal her. She felt her worries seeping away into the earth beneath her feet, replaced by a sense of peace she had long forgotten.

Then, there was John, a man who weathered the storms of life. He carried the weight of loss and grief, his heart heavy with sorrow. It was in he forest that John found solace. The gentle rustling of the leaves, the oft murmur of the brook, and the quiet hum of life all around him all poke to his aching heart. He found comfort in the forest's silent companonship, its quiet understanding. In its infinite patience, the forest llowed him to grieve, heal, and grow.

And so, these stories of resurgence continue, each unique, each profound. They are stories of individuals touched by the healing power of the forest, their lives forever changed. They speak of the transformative experiences of forest bathing, of the renewal and transformation that takes place in its serene depths.

In the forest, the spirit is resurgent, rekindling the soul. It is a place where one can shed the burdens of the past and embrace the promise of the future. It is a place of renewal, of transformation, of resurgence. In these personal stories, we see the true power of forest bathing and the profound impact it can have on our lives.

As we journey deeper into the forest, we continue to uncover these stories, these echoes of resurgence. They are a testament to the enduring call of the forest, a call that resonates within us all.

The Echoes of the Forest: Lasting Impressions of Forest Bathing

In the tranquility of the forest, where the whispers of the wind converse with the rustling leaves, where the sunbeams filter through the verdant canopy to kiss the earth below, there is a profound connection to be made. This connection, once established, leaves an indelible imprint on the soul, a lasting impression that echoes long after one has left the forest's embrace.

These echoes of the forest are not merely memories of a place visited or an activity undertaken. They are the resonances of a deep, transformative experience, a communion with nature that transcends the boundaries of the physical world. They are the silent reminders of the forest's healing power, the gentle nudges towards introspection and self-discovery, and the subtle prompts to slow down, breathe, and be.

Each echo is unique, as unique as the individual who carries it. Fo some, the memory of the forest's tranquility and the serenity envelope them as they bathed in the forest's atmosphere. It is the recollection o the soft rustle of leaves underfoot, the soothing murmur of a distan stream, the gentle caress of the wind. The remembrance of a profoun peace seemed to seep into their very bones, calming their minds, easing their worries, and filling their hearts with quiet joy.

For others, the echo is a sensory memory, a vivid recall of the forest's sights, sounds, and scents. It is the memory of the vibrant foliage greens, the dappled sunlight on the forest floor, and the sudden flash of a bird in flight. It is the recollection of the forest's symphony, the harmonious blend of bird calls, rustling leaves, and the soft sigh of the wind. It is the remembrance of the forest's scent, the earthy aroma of damp soil, the fresh fragrance of leaves, and the subtle perfume of wildflowers.

Yet for others, the echo is a spiritual resonance, a lingering connection with the natural world. It is the memory of a profound sense of belonging, of feeling at one with the forest, tree, leaf, and creature. It is the recollection of a deep sense of awe and wonder, a humbling realization of the grandeur of nature and one's small place within it. It is the remembrance of a profound sense of gratitude, a heartfelt thankfulness for the healing, the peace, and the joy that the forest bathing experience brought.

These echoes of the forest, these lasting impressions, serve as gentle reminders of the transformative power of forest bathing. They are the silent testimonies of the healing embrace of the forest, the quiet affirmations of the profound connections made, and the subtle invitations to return to bathe once more in the forest's tranquil, immersive, and rejuvenating atmosphere. They are the enduring call of the forest, a call that resonates within the heart and is impossible to ignore once heard.

The Enduring Call of the Forest

As our journey through the leafy heart of the forest draws to a close, we find ourselves standing on the threshold of a profound understanding. The enduring call of the forest, a siren song that resonates deep within our souls, is not merely an invitation to step into a world of tranquility and beauty. It is a gentle summons to return to our roots, to reconnect with the primal essence of our being, and to rediscover the healing power of nature that lies dormant within us.

In its timeless wisdom, the forest has whispered its secrets into our hearts. It has shown us that we are not separate from the natural world but an integral part of it. We have breathed in its life-giving air, bathed in its dappled sunlight, and listened to its symphony of sounds. We have felt the earth's pulse beneath our feet and the wind's caress on our skin. We have tasted the sweetness of its fruits and drank from its crystal-clear streams. In these moments of profound connection, we have experienced a sense of peace and well-being that transcends the physical realm, touching the very core of our being.

The transformative experiences of forest bathing are not fleeting moments of bliss but lasting impressions that continue to shape our lives long after we have left the forest. They awaken a deep reverence for nature, a heightened awareness of our surroundings, and a renewed sense of purpose. They inspire us to live more mindfully, to tread more lightly on the earth, and to cherish the precious gift of life.

As we step out of the forest and back into the hustle and bustle of our daily lives, we carry the echoes of the forest with us. We remember the rustle of the leaves, the bird's song, the flowers' fragrance, and the air's stillness. We remember feeling fully present, fully alive, and fully connected to the world around us. And we yearn to return to the forest, bathe once again in its healing embrace, and answer the wild's enduring call.

In the end, forest bathing is more than a practice. It is a way of life, a path to wellness, and a journey of self-discovery. It is a reminder that we are part of a larger whole, a testament to the healing power of nature, and a celebration of the beauty and wonder of the world we inhabit. It is, in essence, a return to the source, a homecoming to the heart of the forest, and a reawakening to the magic and mystery of life itself.

Chapter Summary

- Forest bathing is a practice that invites us to immerse ourselves in nature, allowing its tranquil energy to permeate our being, offering a sanctuary of serenity and healing.
- The first encounter with forest bathing is often a profound awakening, a realization of the deep connection between oneself and the natural world, leading to peace and tranquility.
- The forest invites introspection and self-discovery, providing a safe space for individuals to confront their deepest fears, unfulfilled dreams, and cherished hopes, leading to profound revelations and transformations.
- Forest bathing is an immersive sensory experience, a symphony of nature that awakens the senses and soothes the soul, connecting individuals with nature on a profound level.
- The forest provides a space for a resurgence of the spirit, a rekindling of the soul, where individuals can shed burdens and embrace the promise of the future, leading to stories of renewal and transformation.
- The connection with the forest leaves an indelible imprint on the soul, a lasting impression that echoes long after one has left the forest's embrace, as a reminder of the transformative power of forest bathing.
- The transformative experiences of forest bathing are not fleeting moments of bliss but lasting impressions that continue to shape our lives long after we have left the forest, inspiring us to live more mindfully and cherish the precious gift of life.
- Forest bathing is more than a practice; it is a way of life, a path to wellness, and a journey of self-discovery, reminding us that we are part of a larger whole and celebrating the beauty and wonder of our world.

YOUR CONTINUED JOURNEY INTO THE FOREST'S EMBRACE

As we stand on the precipice of our concluding chapter, let us pause momentarily, like a leaf suspended in the air before it gently descends to the forest floor. We have journeyed together through the heart of the forest, immersing ourselves in its tranquil embrace, and now it is time to reflect on the path we have trodden.

In its infinite wisdom, the forest has been our guide and sanctuary. It has whispered ancient secrets in our ears, secrets that have been carried on the wind, rustling through the leaves and echoing in the peaceful silence of the woodland. We have learned to listen, to listen, to the forest's whisper indeed, and in doing so, we have discovered a profound connection to the natural world and ourselves.

Our journey into forest bathing has been more than just a walk in the woods. It has been a transformative experience, a gentle immersion into the healing power of nature. We bathed in the dappled sunlight filtering through the canopy, breathed in the earthy scent of the forest floor, and felt the cool touch of the breeze on our skin. We have learned to slow down, to be present, and to open our senses to the subtle symphony of the forest.

As we reflect on our journey, we realize that each step we took, each leaf we touched, and each breath we drew in the forest's embrace has left an indelible imprint on our hearts. We have not merely observed the forest; we have become a part of it, and it has become a part of us.

The forest has taught us to see beauty in simplicity, to find peace in silence, and to draw strength from our roots. It has shown us that we are not separate from nature but intrinsically connected to it. It has reminded us of the importance of balance, giving and receiving, growth and decay, light and shadow.

As we stand here, at the end of our journey, we are not the same as we were at the beginning. We have been touched by the forest's whisper, bathed in its healing light, and transformed by its wisdom. We carry the forest within us, and it continues to guide us, to heal us, and to inspire us.

So, let us take a moment to reflect on our journey, honor the wisdom we have gained, and express our gratitude to the forest for its generous gifts. As we turn the last leaf of our journey, let us carry the forest's whisper in our hearts and let it guide us on our continued journey into the embrace of nature.

The Forest's Whisper: Unveiling the Core Insights

As we stand on the threshold of the forest, the whispering leaves beckon us to delve deeper into the heart of our journey. The soft, soothing melody of the forest's whisper has been our guide, leading us through the verdant labyrinth of self-discovery and tranquility. Here, in the stillness of the forest's embrace, we have unearthed the core insights of our journey the major themes, and the findings that have shaped our understanding of forest bathing.

The Forest and Our Well-being

The first theme that emerged was the profound connection between the forest and our well-being. The forest, with its lush canopy and vibrant undergrowth, is not merely a backdrop to our lives but an active participant in our journey toward wellness. The rustling leaves, the chirping birds, the gentle sway of the trees - each element of the forest contributes to a symphony of serenity that calms our minds, soothes our souls and rejuvenates our bodies. Forest bathing is not a mere walk in the woods but an immersive experience that engages all our senses, fostering a deep, holistic connection with nature.

Mindfulness

The second theme that surfaced was the transformative power of mindfulness. Forest bathing is not a passive act but an active engagement with the present moment. It invites us to shed the weight of our worries, let go of our preoccupations, and fully immerse ourselves in the here and now. The forest, with its timeless beauty and tranquil rhythm, serves as a mirror, reflecting our inner state of being. As we attune ourselves to the forest's rhythm, we cultivate mindfulness, a heightened awareness, and presence that transforms our perception of self and the world around us.

Healing Power of the Forest

The third theme that emerged was the universality of the forest's healing touch. Forest bathing is not bound by culture, age, or geography. The forest's embrace is a universal sanctuary, a haven of tranquility that welcomes all seeking solace. Whether it is the towering redwoods of California, the ancient cedars of Japan, or the lush rainforests of Brazil, the healing power of the forest transcends boundaries, offering a shared experience of rejuvenation and renewal.

As we unveil these core insights, we begin to understand the forest's whisper, the subtle yet profound message that it imparts. The forest, in its tranquil majesty, invites us to reconnect with our true selves, cultivate mindfulness, and experience the universal healing power of nature. It is a whisper that echoes in the rustling leaves, the chirping birds, and the gentle sway of the trees, guiding us on our continued journey into the forest's embrace.

The Ripple in the Pond: The Far-reaching Impact of Forest Bathing

As we stand on the forest's edge, gazing into the verdant depths, we are not merely observers but participants in a grand, interconnected dance of life. Forest bathing, as we have journeyed through it, is not an isolated act but a ripple in the pond of our existence, sending out waves of influence that touch every aspect of our lives.

The implications of forest bathing are as vast and varied as the forest itself. It is not merely a practice of relaxation but a profound reconnection with the natural world, a rekindling of our primal bond with the earth. It is a gentle reminder of our place in the grand tapestry of life, a humbling experience that fosters a deep gratitude and respect for the natural world.

The significance of forest bathing extends beyond the individual, reaching into the societal and environmental realms. As we immerse ourselves in the forest's embrace, we are nurturing our well-being and contributing to the health of our communities and the planet. By fostering a deeper connection with nature, we are more likely to care for it, protect it, and advocate for its preservation.

The ripple effect of forest bathing is also evident in its potential to transform our relationship with technology. In an age where screens and devices often dominate our lives, forest bathing offers a much-needed respite, a chance to unplug and recharge in the most natural way possible. It is a gentle nudge towards balance, a reminder of the simple, profound joy of being present in the moment, of truly seeing, hearing, and feeling the world around us.

The forest's whisper is not a solitary voice but a chorus of wisdom, a symphony of insights that resonate far beyond the forest's edge. As we step out of the forest, we carry these lessons with us, spreading the ripple of forest bathing into our daily lives, communities, and the world. The forest's embrace is not a fleeting experience but a lasting imprint, a gentle guide on our continued journey through life.

The Unseen Trail: Addressing Shortcomings and Counterarguments

As we tread the unseen trail, let us pause to acknowledge the limitations and critiques that have emerged along our journey into the forest's embrace. Like the forest itself, the practice of forest bathing is not without its shadows, hidden corners, and unexplored territories.

The first critique often voiced is the lack of empirical evidence supporting the benefits of forest bathing. While numerous studies have suggested a correlation between time spent in nature and improved mental and physical health, the exact mechanisms behind these effects remain largely uncharted. The forest's whisper speaks in a language that science is still learning to decipher.

Another critique lies in the accessibility of forest bathing. Only some have the privilege of living near expansive, untouched woodlands. Urban dwellers, in particular, may find it challenging to immerse themselves in a forest environment regularly. The forest's embrace, it seems, is not universally accessible.

Furthermore, there is the critique of forest bathing being a solitary activity, potentially leading to feelings of isolation or loneliness. While the forest can provide a sanctuary for solitude, it is not inherently solitary. The rustle of leaves, the chirping of birds, and the whispering wind remind us that the forest is a community, a symphony of life.

Lastly, there is the critique that forest bathing is a form of escapism, a retreat from the realities and responsibilities of daily life. We must remember that the forest is not a place to escape but a place to return to. It is not a denial of reality but a reconnection with the reality that we are part of nature, not separate from it.

In addressing these critiques, we must not shy away from them but rather, like the forest, grow from them. We must continue to advocate for more research into the benefits of forest bathing, promote the creation of green spaces in urban areas, encourage communal forest bathing experiences, and reframe our understanding of what it means to return to nature.

As we continue our journey into the forest's embrace, let us remember that every path has its unseen trails, and every practice has its limitations. But it is in acknowledging these that we can truly appreciate the depth and breadth of the forest's whisper and continue to grow, like the forest itself, in wisdom and resilience.

The Seed's Promise: Proposing the Path Forward

As we stand on the edge of the forest, and our journey through the verdant realm of forest bathing draws to a close, we find ourselves cradling a seed. This seed, small and unassuming, holds within it a promise. A promise of growth, renewal, and a deeper connection with the natural world surrounding us. It symbolizes the path forward, a path we must choose to tread in our own time and in our own way.

The forest, with its towering trees and whispering leaves, has shared with us its secrets. It has shown us the power of silence, the beauty of simplicity, and the profound peace that comes from simply being. It has taught us to breathe, listen, and see with new eyes. But the forest's lessons do not end at its borders. They continue in the seed we now hold, which we must choose to plant and nurture in our lives.

Planting this seed may mean different things to different people. For some, it may mean committing to spend more time in nature, regularly immersing oneself in the forest's tranquil embrace. For others, it may mean adopting a more mindful approach to life, learning to slow down, breathe, and truly see the world around them. And for others still, it may mean advocating for protecting and preserving our natural spaces, ensuring that future generations can also experience the healing power of the forest.

Whatever form your seed takes, I encourage you to plant it carefully and intentionally. Nurture it with patience and love. Allow it to grow at its own pace, knowing that, like the forest, it will not be rushed. And as it grows, let it transform you. Let it deepen your connection with the natural world, others, and yourself. Let it bring you peace, joy, and a sense of belonging.

As we part ways, I leave you with this final thought. In all its tranquil beauty, the forest is not just a place. It is a state of being. It is a way of moving through the world with grace, mindfulness, and a deep respect for all life. It is a journey that does not end but continues in the seed we now hold. So, as you step forward from the forest's edge, remember the seed's promise. Remember the lessons of the forest. And remember that no matter where you are, you can always return to the forest's embrace.

ABOUT THE AUTHOR

Naomi Rohan is a devoted author and expert in natural wellness. With a deep-rooted passion for holistic health, she has dedicated her life to exploring and sharing the healing power of nature. Her books, which delve into topics such as forest bathing and earthing, have become essential reading for those seeking to reconnect with the natural world for their well-being.

Naomi's journey began with a degree in the field of natural sciences, which laid the foundation for her understanding of the intricate relationship between humans and nature. She further honed her knowledge through extensive travels, immersing herself in diverse cultures and their unique healing practices.

Naomi's work is characterized by her vivid, expressive writing style and ability to translate complex concepts into accessible, practical advice. She has a unique knack for guiding her readers on a journey of self-discovery and healing, helping them to find balance and harmony in their lives.

When she's not writing, Naomi can be found wandering in the woods, barefoot on the beach, or tending to her herb garden. She continues to be a student of nature, constantly learning, evolving, and sharing her wisdom with the world.

Made in the USA
Las Vegas, NV
10 March 2024

86966711R00075